13/12/02
gay boy

27

D1587468

The Play of Room 13

Joe Standerline

Based on the novel by Robert Swindells

Introduction by Robert Swindells

Series editor: Lawrence Till

Heinemann Educational Publishers
Halley Court, Jordan Hill, Oxford OX2 8EJ
A division of Reed Educational and Professional Publishing Ltd

OXFORD MELBOURNE AUCKLAND
JOHANNESBURG BLANTYRE GABORONE
IBADAN PORTSMOUTH NH (USA) CHICAGO

03 02

10 9 8 7 6 5

ISBN 0 435 23326 2

Original design by Jeffrey White Creative Associates; adapted by Jim Turner
Typeset by 🖝 Tek-Art, Croydon, Surrey
Cover illustration by Stephen Jones
Cover design by Philip Parkhouse Design Consultancy
Printed and bound in the United Kingdom by Clays Ltd, St Ives plc

CONTENTS

INTRODUCTION BY ROBERT SWINDELLS

Back in 1987, a bus full of ten-year-olds from a Bradford middle school arrived at Whitby for a five-day stay. With them were three teachers and a guy who writes fiction for children. They were staying at the Riviera Hotel on the West Cliff, and they knew the following things about the town.

- In the nineteenth century it was a major whaling port.
- The most famous of its whalers was Captain William Scoresby, who invented the crow's nest, a platform fixed to the top of a ship's mast and used as a lookout.
- Captain James Cook lived in Whitby as a young man, and his ship, the *Endeavour,* was built there.
- On the East Cliff stand the ruins of an eight hundred-year-old abbey.
- The German navy shelled the abbey from the sea during the First World War.
- In 1887 Bram Stoker, the author of *Dracula*, was staying in Whitby when he got the idea for his novel.

It was this last fact that interested them most. During the course of their stay, the children discovered that a flight of one hundred and ninety-nine steps leads up to the churchyard of St Hilda's on the East Cliff, where Dracula is said to have lurked, and on to the Abbey Field where the ruins stand. They saw posters advertising ghost walks with the sinister Count himself as the guide, and found a creepy house on the fish quay that you pay to walk through in pitch darkness and be scared out of your wits. And they saw where a part of the town known as Haggerlythe had slid down the cliff and been swallowed by the sea.

These discoveries seethed in the children's imaginations, giving rise to grisly stories they told one another as they lay in their beds at night. Someone had got up to go to the lavatory and, happening to glance through the window, had seen Dracula sitting motionless on a bench in the moonlight watching the hotel. Somebody else had seen a classmate sleepwalking up the dark staircase looking for Room 13, which didn't exist by day. And there was the pupil who'd peeped into a linen cupboard, seen a long table with an open coffin on it and caught the scent of recently disturbed soil. For many of the children, this was their first time away without their parents. A few were beginning to wish they'd stayed at home.

On the last day of the visit, a pupil approached the author and said: 'Mr Swindells, why don't you write a story about us in this hotel, and how Dracula lives here, in a room that's only there at night?'

And that's it: *Room 13*, handed to its author on a plate. The Riviera Hotel became The Crow's Nest, drowned Haggerlythe lent its name to a mysterious old woman, and a few fictional children joined the ones from Bradford so no *real* child was cast as hero or villain. They are there in the story though, the real children. They've grown up now and gone their various ways, but it pleases the author to believe that as long as one copy of the book survives they'll stand together, always ten years old on a windswept clifftop pathway, gazing out to sea.

Bob Swindells

GENERAL INTRODUCTION

When I was at school, I used to hate reading plays. I often found the story confusing and the characters difficult to keep track of. Since then, I'm pleased to say that I've learnt how it's done and I now enjoy it as much as watching a film or a good session in front of the TV.

The great thing about reading a play, as opposed to watching a performance of one, is that all of the action takes place inside your own mind. Before you pick it up, a play is no more than a collection of words. As the writer, it has been my job to come up with these words and, as the reader, it will be your job to bring them to life. How? By applying the power of your imagination.

Adapting a novel into a stage play takes a lot of decision-making. Even though the characters and basic storyline already exist, the playwright still has to decide how to present them to an audience. Are there enough characters? Should the series of events take place in the same order as in the novel? How much of the story should the audience have to work out for themselves? Should the characters be the same ages as they are in the novel? (In the play, the students are from Year 7, which makes them eleven to twelve years old.)

In a novel, a character's feelings can be described to us; we can even be told what he or she is thinking. In a play, however, these things have to be achieved through the character's words and actions. The playwright has to give the audience clues. If you listen to people talking to each other, you'll notice they don't really describe themselves. Even so, you can still get an idea of what sort of people they are. There are also practical considerations when putting a play together. Is there enough time for costume changes? How long will it take to change scenes? How many different locations do there have to be?

I used questions like these to help me write *The Play of Room 13*. I hope you enjoy reading it as much as I enjoyed putting it together. To help you read it, I have provided a few notes beginning on page 63. If you feel the way I used to about reading plays, maybe you should take a look.

Joe Standerline

LIST OF CHARACTERS

Speaking characters

Sally Haggerlythe
A mysterious, ancient-looking character who's even older than her appearance would suggest.

Mrs Marriott
A senior teacher who loves dishing out orders. She speaks in a precise, military manner and won't stand for any nonsense.

Mr Hepworth
An easygoing teacher with more hair in his eyebrows than on his head. He's a bit of a joker but others don't find him as funny as he thinks he is.

Grant Cooper
Pretty gullible and loves a good gossip.

David Trotter
Boisterous and always ready for an adventure.

Waseem Kadeer
Funny, cheeky, rude and troublesome, Waseem always gets found out. He's mates with Grant.

Andrew Roberts
Mr Cool, when he remembers to be.

Mrs Evans
A scatty teacher with a dry sense of humour.

Vicky Holmes
Highly strung with a short fuse and short attention span.

Ellie-May Sunderland
Has long, blonde hair, lives in a huge house and is accustomed to getting what she wants.

Gary Bazzard
*David's best mate. He's pretty infantile but sees himself
as a bit of a hero.*

Lisa Watmough
*Down-to-earth, likes to enjoy herself and doesn't have much
time for idiots.*

Felicity Morgan (Fliss)
Lisa's best friend. Mature, intelligent and witty.

Haley Denton
*Friends with Vicky, but prefers to hang around with the lads.
Bit of a tomboy.*

Maureen Wishard (Mo)
Joanne Wishard (Jo)
*Twin sisters. Kind-hearted, compulsive and loud. They both
have old heads on their shoulders and dream of working in the
fashion industry. They're always willing to help a friend. Mo is
the quieter of the two, but only just.*

The Beast
Needs no introduction!

Non-speaking characters

Two little girls
Other school members
Tall, hooded creatures
The landlady
First World War soldiers

With thanks to Dr David

ACT ONE

Scene One

Soft, haunting organ music fades in. Misty images of Whitby appear on a screen suspended above a dark stage. Included in these are pictures of the old streets, amusement arcades, fishing boats and the Abbey. As the voice-over comes to an end, so the sequence ends with an image of a spooky-looking hotel.

(*voice-over*)

Sally   A lonely house in haunting mist,
To chill a dragon's breath,
Six and seven,
Two on eleven,
Sleeps in the jaws of death.

There stands a tomb
In beastly room,
A child both young and old,
A smell of rot
Beside her cot,
A deed of doom
That will be told.

Scene Two

*Car park in Pickering. Late Monday morning. A
gang of 'school trippers' burst on to the stage.*

Mrs Marriott (*blows her whistle*) Halt. We are a respectable
school, not a gang of troublesome hooligans.
Mr Hepworth.

Mr Hepworth Yes, Mrs Marriott?

Mrs Marriott Head count, if you please.

*Mr Hepworth starts counting. Mrs Evans is quietly
watching over David, Waseem and Grant.*

Grant Come on then, Dave, what happened?

David She got out the car so she could have a look,
right ...

Waseem Hang on, I never heard the first bit.

Grant It happened on that country road we've just been
on. Start again, Dave. (*to Andrew*) Come and listen
to this.

David There's a couple travelling to same place we're
going, for their honeymoon, right ...

Grant They run out of petrol so he has to leave his wife in
the car while he goes to find a garage ...

David Who's telling this?

Mr Hepworth Stand still please, Year 7.

Grant Go on, Dave.

*Andrew takes a comb out, pretending to be more
interested in his hair.*

David She puts the radio on 'cos she's getting bored,
then it comes on the news about this escaped
maniac. Turns out he's from a nut house, close
to here, put there 'cos of all the savage murders
he's done ...

Mrs Evans is getting into the story.

Mr Hepworth   We appear to be one short, Mrs Marriott.

Mrs Marriott   Typical.

David   ... So another hour goes by and it's pitch black outside. By this time, she's terrified. Then, there's this banging on the roof of the car like a thud, thud, thud ...

Mrs Evans is hooked.

David   ... Dents were starting to come in on top of her head and she's screaming.

Andrew   (*as casual as he can make it*) So did he kill her or what?

David   No. It just stopped ...

Mrs Evans looks disappointed.

David   ... But then, a trickle of blood slowly dribbles down the windscreen and when she gets out o' the car to see what's going on ...

Mrs Evans mimes, 'Get on with it!'

David   ... Lying there, on top of the roof ... in one of the dents that the maniac made ...

Andrew
Grant } Yeah!

Mrs Evans is desperate.

David   ... is her husband's head ...

Mrs Evans' eyes widen.

David   ... all battered in and dripping, with veins and stringy stuff hanging out where his neck should've been...

Mrs Evans   (*feeling sick*) That's enough of that, thank you, David.

Waseem   Ahh! She's terrified.

Mrs Evans   Don't be silly, Waseem.

Mrs Marriott blows her whistle once more and Mrs Evans jumps out of her skin.

Mrs Marriott	There appears to be someone missing. Will you all please stop shuffling around so Mr Hepworth can do a recount. Did you hear that, Waseem?
Waseem	Yes, Mrs Marriott. (*to gang*) 'Course, ghost stories aren't scary once you've seen real thing.
Grant	You never have.
Waseem	I have. (*making it up*) It were last year ... No, this year. I were coming home from school when it jumped out at me. It had a robe thing on like an enormous nun and it were screaming.

Mrs Marriott lets rip with another blast on her whistle.

David	Probably Mrs Marriott.

Vicky approaches Mr Hepworth.

Vicky	Sir. Is it true that we're not going to get any free time?
Mr Hepworth	You'll have some, Vicky. Do you know if everyone has come out of the toilets?
Vicky	Think so.
Mrs Marriott	Show a little co-operation. We're still several miles from our destination and there is a lot to fit in this afternoon.

Mrs Evans joins Mr Hepworth.

Vicky	(*to Ellie-May*) See what I mean?
Mrs Evans	Vicky wouldn't be depressed again by any chance, Mr Hepworth?
Mr Hepworth	Frightened she might have to take some of the sights in, Mrs Evans.
Vicky	I thought we were supposed to enjoy ourselves, Miss.
Mrs Evans	Oh, we are Vicky, and we will. Only this afternoon we'll be going to the Church of St Mary ... at the top of a cliff, taking in the Whitby museum, which is much larger than you'd expect and there's the 'whale bone arch' of course. I'm sure you're just dying to see that.

Vicky	(*to herself*) Get me an ambulance.
Ellie-May	Will we have time to get changed before we go out, Mrs Evans?
Mrs Evans	Not if you want to see the Captain Cook monument as well, Ellie-May.
	Vicky looks sick.
Gary	Is he the one that got ate by a crocodile?
Mrs Evans	That's Captain *Hook,* Gary ... and it's 'eaten'. (*to Vicky*) Of course we might be able to fit a few other activities in for you if you're desperate.
Vicky	Can't we just go to the beach and hang around, Miss?
Mrs Evans	What an excellent idea. Did you hear that, Mr Hepworth? Vicky wants a game of rounders on the beach. After such a busy day too. Have we brought the equipment?
	Lisa appears. She is out of breath.
Mrs Marriott	Where do you think you've been, madam?
Lisa	Nowhere, Miss. Sorry, Miss.
Mrs Marriott	Do you want everyone to miss their lunch?
Lisa	No, Mrs Marriott.
Mrs Marriott	What is that?
Lisa	What, Miss?
Mrs Marriott	The article you have stowed beneath your cardigan.
Lisa	It's a torch, Miss. I took it with me in case there wasn't any lights in the toilet.
	Mrs Marriott holds out her hand. Lisa gives her something wrapped in a paper bag. On inspection, it is a torch in the shape of a dragon.
Mrs Marriott	(*unwrapping*) I see. And prior to leaving the coach, you wrapped the offending article in tissue paper and popped it into a paper bag?
Lisa	No, Miss.

Mrs Marriott	What did I say to everyone before leaving the coach?
Lisa	No running off, Miss.
Mrs Marriott	I shall hold on to this unpleasant item until a suitable punishment has been served. What do you say?
Lisa	Thank you, Mrs Marriott.
Mrs Marriott	Back to the coach please, Mr Hepworth.
	Exit Mrs Marriott. Fliss appears and goes over to Lisa.
Mr Hepworth	Right, erm ... You all heard Mrs Marriott.
	They start to file off.
Fliss	What did you do that for? Should've known she'd do her top.
Lisa	Don't know, it was like I had to.
Fliss	But the nearest shop's at the other end of the road. You can't even see it from here.
Lisa	You're getting as bad as Marriott. What's got into you, Fliss?
Fliss	I'm just tired ... I've hardly slept the past couple of nights, been having these really weird dreams.
	Waseem, Gary and Grant pass Mr Hepworth on their way to the bus. Waseem is pulling ghoulish faces.
Mr Hepworth	You'll stay like that, Waseem.
Lisa	(*shouting out*) Be an improvement.
	The others move off, leaving only Fliss and Lisa on stage.
Fliss	Have you been here before?
Lisa	Hard to tell, one car park's pretty much like another ...
Fliss	Whitby, I mean.
Lisa	When I were a baby, me mam said. Why, have you?
Fliss	No, never. Feels like I have, though.
Lisa	Come on, I'm in her bad books enough as it is.

Scene Three

*Organ music fades in. The screen shows two
little girls wearing old-fashioned party dresses
and playing together. Sally's voice sounds over
the action.*

(voice-over)

Sally   Soldiers' rest to family nest,
This blackened house did lay to rest
Both precious days and happiness.
One remains to search in vain,
Shall other e'er be seen again?

Scene Four

*The beach. Monday evening. We hear a climactic
game of rounders being played with cheers,
seagulls and lapping waves. Lights fade up slowly
to reveal the beach. There is a deck chair with a
huge sports bag beside it.*

Haley   *(voice-over)* Come on, Miss, you can do it!

Girls   *(voice-over chanting)* Miss! Miss! Miss!

*There is an almighty cheer. Mrs Evans enters in her
rather extreme rounders outfit. She is exhausted
and slumps into the deck chair. Enter Vicky, Mo
and Jo.*

Mo   That were fantastic, Miss, wa'n't it, Vicky?

Vicky   Mm.

Jo   Ellie-May's right peeved now, Miss, you beat her.

Mrs Evans tries to acknowledge their admiration.
Others start to enter, bats in hand. Vicky stares
at Andrew.

Mo   Them fancy new trainers of hers didn't help much.

Jo   Eighty-five quid an' all.

Mo   And the rest! I'd want to be running for England at
              that price.

Vicky   Andrew's trainers are good.

              Ellie-May comes over.

Jo   Better luck next time, Ellie-May.

Ellie-May My laces came undone.

Mo   Should've got slip-ons, shouldn't she, Joanne.

Jo   They look new, them, Ellie-May. Bet you've brung
              loads of new stuff for trip, an't yer?

Ellie-May Enough.

Jo   We've got our whole summer collection with us
              an't we, Mo.

Ellie-May You mean those disgusting things you make
              yourselves?

Mo   Eh, they're not disgusting.

Ellie-May I'll have to decide that after I've seen them.

Mo   Come and have a look tonight if you like.

Ellie-May I might.

              Ellie-May walks away.

Mo   Wonder she dun't trip over things, way she goes
              about with her snout in the air. You like our designs
              don't you, Vicky?

Vicky   Looks older than twelve, dun't he?

              Mo is confused.

Jo   (*to Mo*) Andrew Roberts. She's got the hots for him.

Vicky   Mrs Marriott did her nut when he climbed on that
              Captain Hook thing.

Mrs Evans   (*recovering*) *Cook*, Victoria.

Vicky   Yes, Miss. (*to twins*) It was hilarious. Laughed that much I were nearly sick.

Mo   Romantic, in't she.

Enter Gary limping.

Mrs Evans   Gary, you've missed the game. What on earth happened?

Gary   Fell down the steps of the Abbey, Miss.

Mrs Evans   All one hundred and ninety-nine of them? Why didn't you say anything earlier?

Gary   Doesn't matter, Miss, looks worse than it is.

Mrs Evans   I've given everyone fifteen minutes to do as they please. Perhaps you should do yours sitting down. (*she stands up, picks up the bag and shouts to the group*) We need to get those poles out of the sand if anyone feels like helping.

Mrs Evans jogs off stage. Everyone pretends to be busy. Jo and Mo decide to go and help. Fliss is facing the auditorium as though looking out to sea. Upstage, the figure of a spindly old woman appears. Fliss becomes uncomfortable and turns around to see the old woman staring back at her. Enter Lisa holding a few sheets of paper. The old woman disappears.

Lisa   You all right?

Fliss   (*looking around*) Suppose.

Lisa   Five hundred lines, just for nipping to the shop. Can you believe that? She couldn't even be bothered to look at 'em either. I can talk to someone else if you want.

Fliss   Sorry, Lise. Don't you think there's something creepy about this place?

Lisa   It's an old town, Fliss, they're all like it.

Fliss   What about the hotel?

Lisa	Funeral parlour more like.
Fliss	I'm sure I've seen it somewhere before.
Lisa	Mr Hepworth said soldiers from the First World War lived in there. Place must be ancient.
Fliss	I think I've dreamt about it.
Lisa	But we haven't been to bed yet.
Fliss	That's what bothers me.

Waseem, David, Gary and Grant come over.

Grant	We've just found a crab, do you want to see it?
Lisa	Not especially.
Waseem	It's got pincers and everything. Got it in one of them pools over there. Show 'em, Grant.

Grant slowly opens his cupped hands.

Grant	Don't make any sudden moves, it might bite me.

He throws his empty hands up to the girls' faces. Exit Fliss, upset.

Lisa	That was mature.
Gary	What's the matter with her?
Lisa	There's a nasty little bug going round and it looks a bit like you.

Exit Lisa same direction as Fliss.

Grant	Told you they'd scream, Waz.

Gary starts to fiddle about with his trousers.

David	(*picking up a leaflet from the sand*) 'The Dracula Experience'?
Grant	Where's that?
David	On the front somewhere. There's a little map on the back. (*reading*) 'Live the horror!' You fancy it?
Waseem	Should be a laugh, yeah.
Grant	What you doing, Gary?
Gary	(*hands down trousers*) Feeling a bit hungry, mate. Is Miss watching?

Waseem I hope not.

Gary pulls out a huge stick of rock from the side of his trousers.

Gary Anyone want a bit?

Grant
Waseem } No thanks!

Scene Five

The Crows Nest. Fliss' hotel room. Monday evening. Jo, Mo and Ellie-May are in their nightdresses. Ellie-May is looking at the clothes they've brought.

Mo I don't see any point in spending hundreds of pounds when you can make things yourself that are just as nice.

Ellie-May picks up a nasty-looking blouse.

Jo Try it on if you like.

Ellie-May isn't sure.

Mo It's Designer.

Ellie-May reluctantly puts it on over her nightie.

Mo Oh, she looks right classy dun't she, Joanne?

Enter Mrs Evans wearing a dressing gown and slippers. She has Vicky with her.

Mrs Evans Another of your creations, girls?

Jo Do you want to try it on an' all, Miss?

Mrs Evans No thank you, Joanne, and I think you should be getting back to your room, Ellie-May.

Ellie-May I'm allowed to stay up till ten at home, Mrs Evans.

Mrs Evans Nine should make a nice change for you in that case.

Ellie-May	(*taking the blouse off and handing it to Mo*) Not too bad, I suppose.
Mrs Evans	Where's Felicity?
Jo	She's in the bog, Miss.
Mrs Evans	I see, she left the hotel and went in search of marsh land ...
Mo	She's having a wash in the lavatory, Miss.
Mrs Evans	Better. You could suggest a sink next time. Bed, girls, please. And Victoria, try to resist loitering on the boys' floor in future.

Exit Mrs Evans.

Vicky	(*embarrassed*) Show up.
Mo	(*to Vicky*) What were you down there for?
Jo	Staring through Andrew Roberts' keyhole.
Vicky	No I wasn't.

Jo mimes 'She was' as Vicky gets into bed. Jo holds up the blouse.

Jo	Where did this come from anyway?
Mo	Found it in the bottom of that wardrobe. Disgustin', in't it.

The twins get into bed. Enter Fliss.

Jo	You took your time.
Fliss	(*climbing into bed*) I've been talking to Lisa. Did Miss say anything?
Mo	No, you're all right. Shall I turn lights off then?
Fliss	If you have to.

Stage goes dark.

Scene Six

The Crow's Nest. Fliss' hotel room. Late Monday night. There is a slow, laborious ticking sound. A blue spot fades up on Fliss. She is asleep. The two little girls from the previous video image appear and start to run around Fliss' bed.

(voice-over)

Sally A lonely house in haunting mist,
To chill a dragon's breath,
Six and seven,
Two on eleven,
Sleeps in the jaws of death.

Fliss wakes suddenly. The little girls have gone.

Fliss Are you asleep?

Fliss lies down again. There is a sinister breathing sound.

Fliss Joanne? Vicky?

The town clock strikes twelve. Very faint organ music drifts in.

Fliss *(sitting up)* Mo? Anyone?

There is creaking. Fliss gets out of bed and leaves the room. In the hall, a door with the number 13 on it is visible. The organ music appears to be coming from the other side of it. Fliss taps lightly then tries to go inside. It's locked. She taps once more. Lights fade up on Room 13. Moonlight streams in through a huge stained glass window in front of which is silhouetted a tall, caped figure (the Beast). A girl with blonde hair, her back to the audience, walks slowly towards him. She's wearing a nightdress and appears to be asleep. The music is much louder now and the sound of Fliss tapping on the other side of the door is amplified to a 'boom, boom, boom'.

The Beast   Come to me, little one.

The girl moves closer as the Beast stretches out his arms.

Fliss   (*her voice echoes wildly inside the room*) Is anyone in there ... ere ... ere ... ere? Hello ... lo ... lo ... lo ...

The girl gets dangerously close to the Beast inside Room 13. At the same time, a second figure appears behind Fliss in the hallway. He approaches Fliss from the shadows and reaches out as if to grab her. Fliss sees him and screams. Room 13 plunges into darkness as the lights become brighter in the hallway. The figure is Mr Hepworth. He is wearing a dark bathrobe with a towel draped over his head.

Mr Hepworth   What are you doing out of bed?

Scene Seven

The Cleveland Way. Late Tuesday morning. Mrs Evans bounds on to the stage wearing hiking gear. She is followed by Waseem, David, Gary, Grant, Haley, Mo and Andrew.

Mrs Evans   The old drovers used to use the Cleveland Way to transport their cattle. It was cheaper than the roads of the time.

Mo   What's a drover, Miss?

Mrs Evans   England's answer to a cowboy, Maureen. It goes all the way round the Hambleton Hills, the Clevelands obviously, and stretches almost as far as Filey.

Haley	So how far's Cleveland?
Mrs Evans	Further than I'm prepared to travel this morning, Haley.
	Enter Mr Hepworth with an assortment of other children including Vicky, Gary and Jo.
Mr Hepworth	Mrs Evans! Some of the children are starting to lag behind.
Mrs Evans	Take five, everyone.
Haley	(*to Andrew*) That's girls for you.
	Vicky slides over to Haley.
Vicky	Boring, in't it.
Haley	Better than sitting in school, I suppose.
Andrew	There's a caravan site over there.
Vicky	(*pretending to see it*) Oh yeah. I love caravan sites, I think they're dead interesting.
	Andrew pulls a face at Haley then moves away slightly.
Haley	You hear about Fliss last night?
Vicky	No, should I have?
Haley	She was sleepwalking. Only woke up in Hepworth's room this morning ...
Vicky	Urgh!
Haley	... while he was taking his pants off.
Vicky	Urrrgh! Wonder she's not in hospital. (*to Andrew*) Have you heard this? Hope I don't end up in one of the lads' rooms. I sleepwalk sometimes.
Andrew	Better keep door locked in that case.
	Andrew goes over to join the lads.
Vicky	(*lets out a painful sigh*) I'm depressed.
Haley	They're not worth it, Vicky.
Vicky	How would you know, you've never had a boyfriend in your life.
Haley	Neither have you.

Enter Fliss and Lisa.

Fliss   There must have been someone in there with him, whoever it was.

Lisa   If you ask me, Fliss, I'd say it was another dream.

Fliss   Mr Hepworth was real enough.

Lisa   You *were* sleepwalking, then.

Vicky   (*to Lisa*) Haven't you heard? Was it horrible, Fliss? Bet it was.

Fliss   I thought ...

Vicky   (*to Lisa*) Hepworth's bad enough at the best of times, never mind in his undies.

Lisa   You kept that bit quiet.

Fliss   He wasn't wearing undies.

Vicky   (*yelps*) I feel sick!

Fliss   He had a bathrobe on. (*to Vicky*) Who's been telling you all this?

Vicky   Waseem.

Lisa   That figures.

Mr Hepworth   Has anyone seen Mrs Marriott?

Gary   She was at the back, Sir.

Mo   Ellie-May's not here either, Sir.

Jo   Maybe they fell off the edge!

Mo   Or Mrs Marriott's sneaked her off to one of them posh little tea shops.

Mr Hepworth   Haley.

Haley   Yes, Sir?

Mr Hepworth   Would you mind running back? See if you can find them.

Haley   OK. (*makes a speedy exit*)

Fliss   (*to herself*) Two on eleven ...

Lisa   Let them worry about who's missing.

Fliss   Mm?

Lisa   Counting, let them worry about it.

Fliss   There was something about the door.

Lisa   You on about that again?

Fliss   It looked different this morning.

Lisa   Like a big cupboard by any chance?

Fliss   This could be serious, Lisa.

Lisa   Snap out of it, will yer? The only numbers on our floor are ten, eleven and twelve. There's no secret room and no *monster* or whatever you *think* it was you heard in there. We're just an ordinary school, on an ordinary trip, in a quaint little fishing village ...

Fliss   It's a town.

Lisa   Whatever. The only *serious* thing going on here is someone who's paying too much attention to some stupid dream she's been having.

Waseem stomps over with his arms out and making snoring noises.

Waseem   Oooh, I'm feeling sleepy. Think I'll go into Mr Hepworth's room and have a look at his grundies.

The lads laugh.

Fliss   (*angry, grabbing Waseem's neck*) Listen, idiot. I was not sleepwalking last night, and the sooner you get that into your thick head the better.

Waseem   (*scared*) Fliss, it's hurting.

A small crowd starts to form.

Fliss   It's supposed to.

Lisa   (*can't quite believe her eyes*) Fliss?

Waseem   Mrs Evans! Felicity Morgan's trying to strangle me.

Mrs Evans   Good for her.

Lisa   You're making his eyes bulge.

Fliss lets go.

Waseem	(*rubbing his neck*) Don't know what you're blaming me for, Dave Trotter's one who started it.
David	Don't be draggin' me into it.
Fliss	(*grabbing David*) Well?
David	Said I'd seen someone sleepwalking, that's all.
	Waseem makes his escape.
Fliss	When?
David	Just before midnight.
Fliss	Who was it?
David	I thought it was you. She had blonde hair and came out of number twelve.
Lisa	That's my room. What were you doing on our floor anyway?
David	Toilet. Someone was having a bath in our one. You gonna let go?
Fliss	(*lets go of him and tries to calm down*) Did you see where she went?
Lisa	(*under her breath*) Wouldn't have been the cupboard by any chance?
	Fliss flashes Lisa a warning glance.
Lisa	Sorry.
David	She went towards there, yeah. Has something been nicked?
Fliss	(*to Lisa*) Who's in number twelve with you?
Lisa	(*exasperated*) Ellie-May, Chantelle and er ... Haley.
	Enter Haley out of breath.
Haley	I found 'em, Mr Hepworth. Ellie-May went all pale and fainted, Sir. Mrs Evans is giving her some tea and trying to get her to stand up. She asked if it was all right for everyone to start their dinners while she brings her over.
Fliss	(*to Lisa*) Now do you believe me?
David	Believe what?

Fliss   We've got some planning to do.

Lights fade. More images of Whitby appear on the screen as Sally's voice fades in.

(*voice-over*)

Sally   There stands a tomb
In beastly room,
A child both young and old,
A smell of rot
Beside her cot,
A deed of doom
That will be told.

Scene Eight

Top floor landing of The Crow's Nest. Late Tuesday night. David and Gary stand outside the closed bathroom door.

David   I hope this is gonna to be worth it.

Fliss appears from Room 11.

Gary   At last. You said to be here for ten to.

Fliss   Something was happening outside. I heard feet dragging on the gravel.

David   Probably a werewolf.

Fliss   I knew it was a mistake to let you two in on it. What's happened to Lisa?

Sound of toilet flushing. David points to the door.

Lisa   (*opening bathroom door*) You can come in now. Hiya, Fliss.

They go into the bathroom.

Lisa   Anything happened then?

David	What do you think?
Lisa	I can smell mints again.

The lads smile at each other. The town clock starts to strike twelve.

Fliss	Ssh. What was that?
Gary	It's that clock in the town.
Lisa	(*to Fliss*) They put Ellie-May in with Mrs Marriott tonight.
David	Talk about teacher's pet.

There is a creaking sound.

Fliss	Ssh! Listen.

Fliss peers out.

Gary	Can you see anything?
Fliss	It's too dark.
Lisa	(*handing Fliss her torch*) Try this.

Fliss takes the torch and shines it around the hall.

David	The door!
Fliss	Which one?

Fliss shines the torch on the doors.

David	That one, look. Something's happening to it.
Lisa	It's sort of changing colour. At the top there, look.
Gary	She's doing it with the torch.
Fliss	I'm not doing anything!

Creaking sound gets louder. The number 13 appears on the door.

David	Tell me I'm not the only one who saw that.
Fliss	Six and seven? That's it. There were numbers in my dream. Those ones, then a two and an eleven.
Gary	What's she on about?
Fliss	Add them together.
Gary	Yeah?

Fliss   And look at the door.

David   Thirteen!

Organ music fades in.

Fliss   It's happening again.

Gary   Get down. It's Marriott!

The door to Room 10 has opened. David, Fliss, Lisa and Gary watch from the bathroom as an entranced Ellie-May walks towards Room 13.

David   It's Ellie-May Sunderland.

Others   Shh!

The door to Room 13 swings inwards with a loud creak.

Beast   (*voice-over*) Come to me, my precious child.

Ellie-May goes inside. The door closes behind her. Lights snap to black and the beam of Lisa's torch shining on the door to Room 13 is the only thing that's visible. A scream tears through the night.

Scene Nine

One of the old-fashioned girls from Scene Three appears on the screen. She looks sad and alone.

(*voice-over*)

Sally   Eyes burn bright through black of night,
And fester deep.
In rise to set,
The truth shall never come to light
While darkness hides in silhouette.

Scene Ten

*Top floor landing of The Crow's Nest. Wednesday
morning. Haley and Vicky are standing outside the
bathroom door.*

Vicky Wonder what bores they've got in store for
us today.

Haley Abbey this morning then a walk to Saltwick Bay,
wherever that is.

Vicky Miles if Miss Evans has anything to do with it.

Lisa comes out of Room 12. She's dressed.

Lisa Is Fliss up yet?

Haley Haven't seen her.

Lisa knocks on the door of Room 11.

Vicky Half an hour they made us look at that whale jaw
thing on Monday. Dead sailors, dead whales ...
dead boring. They're making us walk again today,
Lisa, can you believe it?

Lisa (*not listening*) Great, yeah.

*Knocks again. Mo and Jo come out of
the bathroom.*

Vicky (*rushing in*) I'm busting. See you down there.

Fliss comes out of Room 11.

Haley (*to Lisa*) You'd better get a move on, they've
started breakfast.

Lisa We'll be down in a minute.

Exit Haley.

Lisa (*to Fliss*) Have you forgotten?

Fliss I've just woken up. Mo! Do you mind making my
bed for me? I've got to do something. I'll do both of
yours tomorrow, OK ... ?

Jo approves the deal.

Mo   OK.

Jo and Mo go into Room 11.

Fliss   Have you been in yet?

Lisa   I was waiting for Mrs Marriott to go downstairs.

Mr Hepworth (*off*) Waseem Kadeer. Get that off your head and get a move on.

Waseem   (*off*) But Sir . . .

Mr Hepworth (*off*) Now, thank you.

Fliss   Quick. I'll keep a lookout.

Lisa goes into Room 10. Mr Hepworth enters.

Mr Hepworth Not dressed yet, Felicity?

Fliss   I woke up a bit late, Sir.

Mr Hepworth Hope you're not coming down with the same thing as Ellie-May.

Fliss   Sir. If you knew something had happened to someone, but it would sound stupid if you said anything, would you still say it?

Mr Hepworth I think you'd better tell me.

Fliss isn't sure.

Mr Hepworth If this is about Ellie-May, I think I should know about it, don't you?

Fliss   You'll think I'm stupid.

Mr Hepworth Try me.

Fliss   (*points to cupboard door*) She went in there last night and I think something happened.

Mr Hepworth Are you trying to wind me up, Felicity Morgan?

Fliss   No, Sir. She went in there and there was all sorts of horrible noises . . .

Mr Hepworth Coming from the linen cupboard? A swarm of killer pillowcases, perhaps?

Fliss   I said you'd think it was stupid.

Mr Hepworth	Take a look, shall we?
	Mr Hepworth pulls the cupboard door. Lisa appears from Room 10. She looks terrified. She attracts Fliss' attention without Mr Hepworth seeing.
Mr Hepworth	(*about to turn around*) She'd have needed an axe to get in here ...
Fliss	It opened inwards, Sir. Try pushing it.
	She gesticulates to Lisa, who darts back into Room 10.
Mr Hepworth	I think you should hurry and get dressed before I lose my sense of humour.
Fliss	I definitely saw her go in there. It might just be a cupboard now but it wasn't last night. It was a proper room with a window and everything.
Mr Hepworth	You're serious? (*thinks for a moment*) Wait here.
	Mr Hepworth exits. Fliss knocks on the door of Room 10 and Lisa bursts out.
Lisa	Has he gone?
Fliss	For the minute. How is she?
Lisa	(*upset*) You'll never believe this. I went up to the bed and tapped her on the shoulder. (*even more upset*)
Fliss	What?
Lisa	She turned round and ... it was horrible, Fliss ...
	Jo and Mo come out of Room 11.
Mo	(*to Jo*) Hope it's not kippers again. I can still taste them we had yesterday.
Jo	(*to Fliss*) We've done it.
	Fliss forces a smile. Jo and Mo exit. Lisa waits until they're out of sight.
Lisa	There was blood, Fliss. Two small dots on the side of her neck!
Fliss	Blood?

Mr Hepworth	(*off*) Morning, girls.
Jo **Mo**	(*off*) Morning, Sir.
Fliss	Stay calm.

Lisa panics and eventually rushes back into Room 10. Mr Hepworth appears with a key on a piece of string. He unlocks the cupboard and pulls the door open. There are shelves inside full of towels, sheets and pillowcases.

Mr Hepworth	Satisfied?
Fliss	Maybe there's something behind the shelves?
Mr Hepworth	Yes, an external wall.
Fliss	But the window.
Mr Hepworth	Your imagination, Felicity.

Fliss tries to speak.

Mr Hepworth	I can see you're upset. Dreams can appear very real sometimes. That's all it was. Get yourself dressed. You might still make breakfast if you hurry.
Fliss	I'm not hungry, Sir.
Mr Hepworth	Make sure you're ready by half past, we'll be leaving for the Abbey then. And Felicity?
Fliss	Sir?
Mr Hepworth	I don't want to hear any more of this.
Fliss	No, Sir.

Exit Mr Hepworth.

Fliss	(*opening the door to Room 10*) OK.
Lisa	(*re-entering*) She looks awful, Fliss. She keeps drifting off then she'll wake up again and claw at her skin. She can't remember anything about last night, I asked her. Do you think we should tell one of the teachers?
Fliss	No point.

Scene Eleven

The screen displays a 'fast motion' journey from the bottom of the one hundred and ninety-nine steps, up to the grounds of the Abbey. It is Wednesday lunchtime. Lights come up on stage. Mrs Marriott is giving the group a talk as they stand among the Abbey ruins.

Mrs Marriott   ... stones that surround you are what remains of the West Wall. Sadly, this collapsed in 1794, taking the magnificent West Window with it.

Haley puts her hand up.

Mrs Marriott   Yes, Haley?

Haley   Is there any of the Abbey that's still in one piece?

Mrs Marriott   Only what you see around you.

Vicky   Whoopi-do.

Mrs Marriott   In fact, it's a miracle there's anything here at all. So far, this site has managed to withstand the ravages of the Danes, Vikings, Henry VIII and the Imperial German Navy.

Fliss sees something and stares into the distance.

Mrs Marriott   There was also that other famous visitor, of course. Who can tell me anything about Bram Stoker?

Mo   Did he keep the Abbey's fire going, Miss?

Mrs Marriott   No, Maureen. He wrote the first-ever version of the Dracula story, drawing inspiration from this mysterious little town you see below us ...

As Mrs Marriott continues, audience attention is taken by Fliss. She has spotted something and starts to sneak away from the group.

Lisa   (*whisper*) Where you going?

Fliss   Shh! Won't be long.

Exit Fliss.

Mrs Marriott . . . creeping inland to engulf the surrounding shoreline. Some say it carries the souls of drowned fishermen . . .

Grant What was it called again?

Mrs Marriott It's called 'The Har', Cooper. Please pay attention. These days it is usually referred to as 'The Whitby Mist'.

Enter Mr Hepworth carrying two heavy-looking carrier bags. He is exhausted.

Mrs Marriott Ah, just in time. Form an orderly line in front of Mr Hepworth.

Mr Hepworth hands out bags of chips to everyone. Sally appears in the spotlight. She is standing in front of a stone wall on the other side of the stage. Enter Fliss.

Fliss (*unsure*) Hello.

Sally Af'noon.

Fliss I'm staying at The Crow's Nest.

Sally Aye, I know.

Fliss Did I see you out in the garden last night?

Sally Depends where you were looking.

Fliss I thought I saw you through the window in my room.

Sally Eyes of a house are winders.

Fliss (*trying her best*) Yes. Quite a lucky one that, looking out on to such a beautiful view.

Sally Nowt lucky about that place. Got the other eye. Watches through night then fades to nothing at sunrise. No good has ever come of that place.

Fliss (*confused*) I suppose not.

Sally No *suppose* about it.

Fliss I should get back. Nice talking to you.

Fliss turns to leave.

Sally Mind yourself. Old stones o'er yonder are not as true as they once were.

Fliss (*turning back*) Thanks. See you then.

Fliss exits, wondering why she'd gone over there in the first place.

Sally That you will, lass.

Sally fades from view. The group are now tucking into their fish and chips. Andrew plonks himself down next to Waseem, Grant and Haley.

Waseem (*to Andrew*) What's up with you?

Andrew Hepworth put vinegar on. I hate vinegar.

Grant Why don't you give 'em to Vicky?

Andrew She can get stuffed.

Haley You told everyone?

Andrew What if I have?

Haley But you promised. She's great, Vicky. You'd like her if you talked to her a bit.

Andrew No chance.

Waseem Bad for your health, girlfriends are.

Haley And how do you work that out?

Waseem My dad told me. From the first day you get a girlfriend your hair starts dropping out.

Haley Rubbish.

Grant It'll be right, his dad's a doctor in't he, Waz.

Waseem Yup ... and the more you go out with, he says, the faster it drops.

Haley (*to Waseem*) You'll be all right then.

Andrew (*screwing up chip wrapper*) Anyone want these?

Re-enter Fliss. She goes over to Lisa, Gary and David who are now sitting in front of a large piece of fallen masonry.

Gary I still say it's Dracula in there.

Lisa   Dracula's just a story, Gary.

David Yeah, but it was taken from real life, Mrs Marriott said. That fella from Transylvania who stuck people on spikes and caused everyone to have a blood shortage. It could be him up there.

Fliss (*approaching*) Did you save me some?

Lisa   (*handing Fliss a bag of chips*) So where did you sneak off to?

Fliss You don't want to know.

Lisa   I can't stop thinking about her.

Fliss Marriott asked the landlady to keep an eye on her.

David If she's not too busy sharpening spikes.

Lisa   What?

Fliss Ignore him.

Waseem and Grant jump on to the stone the others are leaning against and scare them half to death.

Grant We know something you don't know.

Gary   Like what?

Waseem What's it worth?

Lisa   A smack in the teeth?

Waseem Crabby!

Grant Hepworth said there might be a disco tomorrow night.

Lisa   (*to Fliss*) Big deal.

A piece of the stone that Waseem and Grant are standing on breaks away and falls on to the ground beside Fliss.

Fliss Look what you've done, you idiots.

Grant It's only a bit of old rock.

Lisa   That's part of the Abbey. We'll get slaughtered if Marriott finds out ...

Mrs Evans (*from a distance*) Misters Cooper and Kadeer, a word if you please.

Waseem	Don't say owt, will yer.
Gary	What's it worth?
Mrs Evans	(*from a distance*) Am I talking to myself?
	Grant and Waseem sheepishly go over to Mrs Evans. Fliss squeezes the stone fragment into her coat pocket.
Lisa	So what are we going to do? Any ideas?
David	I say we tell her.
Gary	She means about Ellie-May, you dingbat.
Mrs Marriott	(*blows on her whistle*) Gather round, Year 7, and bring your chip wrappers with you.
Fliss	Meet at the same time tonight. I've got an idea.
	The group assemble by the teachers.
Mr Hepworth	Maureen and Joanne are walking round with rubbish bags. Please see that you use them.
Mrs Marriott	Make sure you have all of your belongings with you; we'll be making our way over to Saltwick Bay presently. I suggest we adopt a leisurely pace this afternoon, Mrs Evans, I'm sure our fellow tourists do not wish to witness the synchronized vomiting of fish and chips. Is there something wrong with you, Felicity?
Fliss	No, Miss.
Mrs Marriott	Then why are you stooping?
Fliss	I've got a pebble in my pocket, Miss. Got it from the beach this morning.
Mrs Marriott	Then I suggest you put it down, we have a long walk ahead.
Fliss	I want to keep it.
	Gasps from the group.
Lisa	(*whisper*) Fliss!
Mrs Marriott	I beg your pardon?
Fliss	I want to keep it, Mrs Marriott. It's for my geography project.

Mrs Marriott   (*deciding to relent*) You're the one who has to carry it for the next five miles.

Vicky   Five!

David   (*to Lisa*) She's letting her off. I don't believe it.

Mr Hepworth   (*to Fliss*) I don't know what's got into you these past few days.

Grant   She's been breathing that Whitby Mist, Sir. It's made her demented.

Mr Hepworth   You must have had your fair share, Cooper.

Grant   Least I don't sneak off and talk to bare walls, Sir. (*to Fliss*) Not like some people.

Fliss is stunned. Lights fade to black as Sally's voice fades over.

(*voice-over*)

Sally   Soldiers rest to family nest,
This blackened house did lay to rest
Both precious days and happiness.
One remains to search in vain,
Shall other e'er be seen again?

Scene Twelve

Top floor landing of The Crow's Nest. Late Wednesday night. David, Gary, Fliss and Lisa are in the bathroom. Lisa is by the door with her torch. We hear a trickling sound, which turns out to be David using the toilet.

Fliss   Can we open our eyes yet?

Lisa   You're disgusting.

David   You had one last night.

Lisa Not with everyone in there, I didn't.

David I feel shattered. Think I'd still be asleep if it wa'n't for Gaz here. Don't know how you stayed awake.

Gary Got my stick of rock, haven't I. Sucked on that from ten o'clock, didn't nod off once.

Fliss I don't know how you can.

David You should see it, though. He's getting a real good point on it now.

Lisa Dirty pig.

The town clock begins to strike twelve.

Gary Get back!

Once again, the number 13 appears on the cupboard door. Faint organ music fades in.

David What if she doesn't come out?

Fliss We're all right then, aren't we.

The door to Room 10 is opening. Ellie-May walks out into the hall.

Lisa She looks green.

Fliss Is everybody ready?

Gary She's getting close!

Lisa Now, Fliss!

Fliss (*quiet call*) Ellie-May!

Ellie-May carries on walking towards Room 13.

Gary Louder, Fliss.

Fliss Ellie-May, over here!

The door to Room 13 swings inwards with the familiar creak.

Lisa It's no use.

They go over to Ellie-May. David and Gary try to pull the door closed. Fliss stands in front of Ellie-May.

Fliss Don't go in there, Ellie-May. Listen to me!

Ellie-May (*hissing, evil voice*) Get your hands off me.

Fliss	Ellie-May! Listen!
	Without effort, Ellie-May throws Fliss to the floor.
Lisa	We're trying to help you. If you go in there, you'll die!
Ellie-May	(*snarling*) Never die. Never die.
Beast	(*off*) Come to me, my precious child …
Gary	It's no good, it's not going to budge.
	Lisa grabs hold of Ellie-May from behind. Fliss is now back on her feet.
Lisa	Help me, Fliss, I can't hold her!
David	I'll keep trying, go and help the girls.
	Gary and Fliss both take hold of Ellie-May.
Beast	(*off*) Release the child …
David	(*looking into Room 13*) I can see him!
Gary	Get her down.
	They fight Ellie-May to the floor and she begins to buck and scream.
Beast	The child belongs to me.
David	He's heading for the door!
	David pulls with all his might. Fliss, Lisa and Gary struggle to keep Ellie-May on the ground. They look towards the open door and scream. Ellie-May becomes still as a light comes on in the hallway. The door to Room 13 closes, throwing David to the floor. Mrs Marriott enters, followed by Mr Hepworth and Mrs Evans.
Mrs Marriott	What in heaven's name do you think you're doing?

ACT TWO

Scene One

Sally appears on the video screen. She is standing in front of the Abbey and looking out to sea.

(*voice-over*)

Sally Nature's law is disobeyed,
She walks in sickly-sweet decay.
Those brought to break the wicked fate
That tears a child apart
Cannot debate with living hate,
Though may outsmart
A broken heart.

Scene Two

It is Thursday. Early afternoon. Scene opens on a street in Whitby with the group assembling outside 'The Dracula Experience'. The coach is nearby on which Fliss, David, Gary and Lisa have had to sit all morning.

Mo I thought it were right beautiful. Din't you, Joanne?

Jo I did, yeah.

Mo Way that little street just disappears into sea. It's like sommat out a fairy story.

Jo One school got their bus stuck down it, I saw a picture.

Mo	Shame to leave, really. What were it called again?
Vicky	Robin Hood's 'borin'' Bay.
Mo	Sorry I spoke.
Jo	She's upset. Andrew Roberts called her a . . . (*whispers in Mo's ear*)
Vicky	Tell everyone, why don't you.
Haley	He's an idiot, Vicky, why don't you just forget him?
	Vicky mumbles something.
Haley	You what?
Jo	She loves him, she said.
	Vicky rolls her eyes.
Mo	Maybe you should tell him.
Vicky	How? He won't even look at me.
Jo	I think we can sort that out. We can do her up for disco tonight.
Haley	If we're still allowed to have one.
Vicky	I felt ashamed for that lot at breakfast. Marriott went on at 'em for hours. Show up or what.
	Mrs Evans has arrived and she's listening in.
Mo	Whatever possessed 'em to have a game of rounders at that time?
Haley	Outside Marriott's room an' all, they must be mental.
Mo	(*looking off-stage*) Ooh, they're getting let off the coach.
Vicky	I'd have freaked if she'd made me sit on that thing all morning.
Mrs Evans	Better than Robin Hood's 'borin'' Bay though, surely, Vicky?
	Vicky feels ashamed once again.
Grant	Ready then, Waz?
Waseem	Too right. (*to Andrew*) Suppose you heard what happened last night?

Andrew	Rounders or something stupid.
Waseem	That's what they wanted us to believe.
Grant	They was kicking Ellie-May's head in.
Andrew	Dave and Gaz Bazzard? They'd never hit a lass.
Grant	Nah, but Fliss Morgan would . . .
Waseem	'Specially now she's been possessed.
Grant	She made lads hold her down while she did it. In't that right, Waz?
Waseem	Yup.
Andrew	Doesn't look very possessed from here.
	Enter Fliss, Lisa, Ellie-May, David, and Gary. They all look a little sheepish.
Mrs Evans	Right, this is the moment you've all been waiting for. You are free to wander round and spend what's left of your pocket money.
Mr Hepworth	You must stay on the sea front, on *this* side of the bridge.
	Mrs Marriott enters and joins the other teachers.
Mrs Marriott	There's to be no crossing into the old town, is that understood?
Others	Yes, Mrs Marriott.
Mrs Marriott	Mrs Evans, Mr Hepworth and I will be keeping our eyes open, and we do not expect to see anyone charging along the pavements.
Mr Hepworth	There are other people here besides yourselves, remember.
Mrs Evans	(*as though in pain*) And please everyone, seaside shops can be full of cheap and nasty rubbish, so think before you buy. There are some nice things out there. A gift is something to be proudly displayed, not discreetly disposed of.
Mrs Marriott	(*blows her whistle*) You have two hours!
	The crowd disperses noisily.

Grant	(*to Fliss*) Coming in then, Fliss?
Fliss	I might.
Grant	(*to David*) Dave?
David	No chance.
Grant	We said lasses'd be too scared didn't we, Waz.
David	Yeah, except I'm not a lass.
Waseem	Could've fooled me.
Fliss	What makes you think *I'm* scared?
Waseem	Sound of your knees knocking gives it away a bit. Are you ready, lads?

Andrew and Grant get their money ready.

Fliss	I'll catch you up, Lise.
Lisa	Don't tell me you're going in. Are you mad?
Fliss	After what we've been through, I think I can handle a few plastic skeletons.
Lisa	But we're supposed to be looking after Ellie-May . . .
Fliss	I won't be long. You'd better go over, she's with Marriott. I'll meet you in twenty minutes.
Lisa	Where?
Fliss	That shop with the glass ducks. I'm gonna get one for my mum.

Fliss joins the queue for 'The Dracula Experience'. Lisa goes over to Ellie-May and Mrs Marriott.

Mrs Marriott	(*to Ellie-May*) . . . Are you sure, Ellie-May?
Ellie-May	I must have been sleepwalking, Mrs Marriott. If I was playing rounders, I certainly don't remember it.
Mrs Marriott	That may be the case, but I could hardly punish the others and not you. (*seeing Lisa*) Talk of the devil. I shall be keeping a very watchful eye on you this afternoon, young lady.
Lisa	Yes, Miss.
Mrs Marriott	Where are the other three?

Lisa	Felicity's over there and the boys went in the direction of the arcade, Mrs Marriott.
Mrs Marriott	Typical.
Lisa	Do you want to look round the shops with us, Ellie-May?
Ellie-May	I'm going to look around with Mrs Mar . . .
Mrs Marriott	That is a kind offer, Ellie-May, but I'm afraid I have some important business to attend to.
Ellie-May	(*to Lisa*) All right then.

Lisa and Ellie-May exit. Mr Hepworth and Mrs Evans come over to Mrs Marriott.

Mr Hepworth	Black Horse?
Mrs Marriott	The Duke of York, Mr Hepworth (*looking at her watch*) They have a Happy Hour.

Teachers exit. Lights fade to black.

Scene Three

The stage is dark. Fliss, Waseem, Grant, Andrew and Haley are inside 'The Dracula Experience'.

Haley	(*echoing voice-over*) Fliss!
Fliss	(*echoing voice-over*) Over here.
Haley	(*echoing voice-over*) Keep talking so I can find you.
Waseem	(*echoing voice-over*) Shouldn't be difficult.
Fliss	(*echoing voice-over*) Watch it, you.
Grant	(*echoing voice-over*) This is a rip-off, you can't even see anything.
Andrew	(*echoing voice-over*) Let go of my jacket, Waz.

Waseem   (*echoing voice-over*) I'm over here, mate.

Fliss   (*echoing voice-over*) Haley, is that you?

Haley   (*echoing voice-over*) Are you standing on something, Fliss?

Andrew   (*echoing voice-over*) Grant!

Grant   (*echoing voice-over*) What?

Andrew   (*echoing voice-over*) Let go!

Grant   (*echoing voice-over*) Must be one of the lasses, Andy.

Andrew   (*echoing voice-over*) You're not funny.

Grant   (*echoing voice-over*) I'm nowhere near, how can it be me?

Andrew   (*echoing voice-over*) Waz, then.

Wazeem   (*echoing voice-over*) Hang on. If Haley's with Fliss, and Grant and Andy aren't near each other . . .

Andrew   (*echoing voice-over*) What?

Waseem   (*echoing voice-over*) . . . Who's got hold of my hands?

Dim, coloured lights flash on. Smoke lies heavy at their feet. Each of the cast is standing by a tall, hooded creature. Everyone screams. They try to run but don't seem to get anywhere. Lights flash on and off as an even more ghoulish creature appears. They run around in terror, with haunting screams and hideous laughter ringing in their ears. Suddenly, it all stops. Everything is dark and silent.

Fliss   Haley . . . Grant? . . . Andy?

Sally appears on the stage in a pool of light in front of Fliss. Fliss screams.

Sally   It's all right, lass. Sit thee sen down. Time we had a talk.

A chair appears in another beam of light.

Fliss   Who *are* you?

Sally   Sally . . . what's left of her, anyway. Sit.

Fliss   (*sits*) Why do you keep . . .?

Sally   Tha'd do well just to listen. Stories have changed
            from one age to another but truth remains. A
            terrible truth. He's up there, feeding from youngens
            and there's only one way to stop it. From way
            back, there's bin' talk of chambers there, hidden
            behind empty walls. Rooms inside of windows that
            should look into empty space.

Fliss   That sounds like Room 13.

Sally   Abbey played host to it first. Folk who'd claimed to
            have seen him there would soon vanish. Some say
            great wall were destroyed by townsfolk, others
            believe it were ancient ruins themselves, trying to
            put an end to the horrors that had taken possession.
            Great West Wall came crashing down. Old window
            had gone and so had the Beast from inside it.

Fliss   He went to The Crow's Nest?

Sally   They'd just finished building it then.

Fliss   All those years ago. Didn't the army have it at
            one point?

Sally   Aye, soldiers were in there before we were.

Fliss   You?

Sally   I were a little girl then.

Fliss   Did you see him?

Sally   I saw him all right. Got our Margaret first, then he
            turned on me.

Fliss   You've been in there?

Sally   I had will enough to fight it at first. Tried to bring
            our Margaret out of there, but he had her by then.
            So much pain for one so little. Took all my strength
            to keep out of there. Never got the chance to make
            me all his own, but he still calls. All these years, his
            blood stinging in my veins. As each day passes, he
            becomes harder to resist. So many youngens to
            feed on up there. It makes him stronger.

Fliss   Can't you run away or something?

Sally   And leave our Margaret?

Fliss   She's still alive?

Sally   She still exists. There's only one escape. The child. Has he kept her with him?

Fliss   Ellie-May? No, she's outside . . . How did you know?

Sally   Then there's hope. Once destroyed, them he's taken for his own will die. Your friend has yet to be turned.

Fliss   You're going to kill it?

Sally   No, lass, that deed is yours.

Fliss   I can't do it. What about Ellie-May and all the others? You said they'll die if . . .

Sally   For them he's changed, death will come as a blessing. (*becomes weak*) Slay the Beast and you free their souls.

Fliss   But Ellie-May –

Sally   The lass will live if Beast is defeated.

Fliss   Your sister won't.

Sally   (*in pain*) She's suffered enough. You've been chosen, Felicity. (*she doubles over in pain*)

Fliss   What's happening to you?

Sally   My fight has come to an end. Be brave, lass, don't let him win.

Fliss   You're dying?

Sally   Not before time.

Fliss   What am I supposed to do?

Sally   Listen and you'll be told. If you succeed, your friend will go free and I'll be with my sister once again.

Fliss   But how?

Sally   You will be told.

Sally falls to the ground. The lights begin to fade.

Fliss Sally?

As Sally's body fades from view, an image of The Crow's Nest appears on the video screen above. As the verse is re-told, the camera pans to one of the windows. Sally is looking out.

(voice-over)

Sally There stands a tomb
In beastly room,
A child both young and old,
A smell of rot
Beside her cot,
A deed of doom
That will be told.

Scene Four

Outside 'The Dracula Experience'. The group are gathering with the things they've bought. Ellie-May is laden with expensive-looking things. Mo and Jo are holding bags from charity shops.

Mo Spent up by the look of it, Ellie-May, must have cost a fortune that lot.

Ellie-May Not really.

Jo Nice to see her up and about again, in'it, Mo?

Ellie-May There's nothing wrong with me. I wish you'd mind your own business.

Jo I was only saying.

Mo Can we have a look at what you got?

Ellie-May No, I've had them gift-wrapped.

Ellie-May leaves them.

Jo   Get a load of her. (*to Mo*) How did you get on anyway?

Mo   There's enough to work with. Make-up was a bit pricey here, so I went for glue and a tube of glitter. Did you find sommat for Dad?

Jo   Eventually, wa'n't easy, mind, you know how fussy he is. (*getting the presents out*) I remembered what Mrs Evans said anyhow and ended up getting these. (*shows them to Mo*) . . . Packet of plastic biscuits and a mug with a frog at the bottom.

Mo   Lovely, yeah.

Lisa and Ellie-May enter. Ellie-May is loaded down with shopping. Lisa rushes over to David and Gary.

Lisa   Have you seen Fliss?

David   Not since she went in there.

Lisa   I don't believe it. Teachers'll be back any minute.

Gary   Do you want me to go in and ask?

David   She won't be there now. We've got a couple of minutes, I'll see if I can find her. Hold this for us, Lisa.

Davids hands Lisa a plastic kite then exits. Waseem and Grant come over to Gary and Lisa.

Waseem (*to Lisa*) Where's mistress of the dark then? Busy sinking her fangs into someone?

Lisa   Oh look, it's that little boy, Gary. The one that came running out of 'The Dracula Experience' crying for his mummy.

Waseem No I didn't!

Lisa   Scared of the little ghosties, were you?

Grant   Scared of you more like.

Lisa   Grow up.

Waseem grabs the kite and runs. He and Grant throw it to each other as Gary tries to get it back. Fliss enters. She looks exhausted.

Gary Fliss!

Lisa and Gary go over to her.

Lisa Where've you been?

Fliss The old woman was in there. The one we keep seeing.

Gary The one *you* keep seeing?

Lisa Shut up, Gaz.

Fliss She knows about Room 13. The same thing happened to her sister that happened to Ellie-May. She's in trouble . . .

Mrs Evans enters at the same time as David. He's out of breath.

Mrs Evans Cutting it a little fine weren't we, Mr Trotter?

David Yes, Miss.

Mrs Evans Mrs Marriott and Mr Hepworth will be meeting us back at The Crow's Nest. This is not an excuse for you to give me a difficult time. Is that understood?

Group Yes, Mrs Evans.

Mrs Evans Grant Cooper, what was the last thing I said before we went off to do our shopping?

Grant I don't know, Miss.

Mrs Evans I warned everybody not to spend their money on cheap and rubbishy goods . . .

Grant It's not mine, Miss. I'm holding it for someone.

Grant shoves the now torn and battered-looking kite back at Lisa.

Lisa (*handing it back to David*) Sorry.

Mrs Evans (*hiccup*) So, the nasty little acquisition was yours, Mr Trotter?

David Miss?

Gary She means you bought it.

Mrs Evans How much?

David Three seventy-five, Miss.

Mrs Evans   Three seventy-five for a sheet of polythene and two plastic sticks. Didn't you see how flimsy it was?

David   No, Miss.

Jo   Could've made one o'them.

Everyone looks at Jo. She shrugs.

Mrs Evans   Why do I bother? First there was Lisa Watmough, risking life and limb for that hideous-looking flashlight. Then Gary Bazzard spends I don't know how much on a stick of rock the size of a telegraph pole. Didn't think I knew about that did you, Gary? I've seen it. Poking out from under your bed with an unpleasant beard of fluff stuck to the end of it. It's a wonder any of you ever have any money at all, the way you spend. (*hiccup*) For your own good, I only hope that next time – if there is a next time – you'll be told!

Fliss gasps.

Mrs Evans   I beg your pardon, Felicity?

Fliss   Nothing, Miss.

Mrs Evans   It'll be tea time in thirty minutes. Followed by the ritual torture your kind call a disco.

Cheers.

Mrs Evans   Make sure you get your holiday journals finished tonight. You are to give them to Mr Hepworth as you go in.

Ellie-May   What about make-up, Mrs Evans?

Mrs Evans   I'm not sure he uses the stuff.

Others laugh.

Mrs Evans   Let's see if we can reach The Crow's Nest without buying the remainder of Whitby.

People start to file off. Lisa, Fliss, David and Gary hang back.

David   (*to Fliss*) So, where were you?

Fliss   (*to herself*) You'll be told.

Lisa	(*to David*) Talking to some old woman in there.
Fliss	It's some sort of clue, it has to be.
David	Do you mind letting me in on this?
Fliss	She was talking about putting a stop to everything . . .
Gary	The old woman?
Fliss	I asked her how to do it and that's what she said.
Gary	'You'll be told.' Not very helpful was she?
Fliss	We're the only ones that know the real story about Ellie-May and you've all been told off for buying something that you shouldn't have. Don't you think that's too much of a coincidence?
Grant	Not really.
Lisa	And where do *you* fit in?
David	Marriott had a go at her for that chunk of Abbey she sneaked.
Fliss	That proves it!
Gary	Proves what?
Fliss	It's some sort of sign.
Mrs Evans	(*off*) Perhaps the four of you would like to sit on the coach this evening also.

They exit. On the screen, pictures of the gang arriving back at The Crow's Nest appear.

Sally	(*voice-over*) Eyes burn bright through black of night, And fester deep. In rise to set, The truth shall never come to light While darkness hides in silhouette.

Scene Five

*Thursday evening. The Crow's Nest. Top floor
landing. Fliss, Lisa and Gary are talking. Gary is
sucking on his pointed stick of rock.*

Lisa You'll get slaughtered if you're caught up here.

Fliss Do you have to use that word?

Gary They're all preening themselves for tonight, I can't
be bothered. They're all a gang of kids anyhow.

Haley pops her head out of Room 12.

Haley Is Cleveland with an 'e, a' or 'e.v.e.'?

Fliss Second one.

Haley Thanks. (*goes back in*)

Lisa So if they're a gang of kids, what does that thing
make you?

Fliss Hope you washed it first.

Grant (*off*) Gaz, you up there?

Gary Yeah. What is it?

Grant (*off*) Andy wants to know if he can borrow some
of your hair gel.

Andrew (*off*) No, I don't.

Gary It's in my bag, just take it, Grant.

Grant (*off*) Thanks, mate.

Lisa Have you decided what we should do, then?

Fliss Why have I always got to decide?

Lisa You're the one with all the *clues*, remember?

Gary I think we should ask Marriott to lock her bedroom
door tonight, stop Ellie-May from getting out again.

Fliss Good thinking.

Lisa For once! I don't know why we can't just enjoy

	ourselves. We're leaving tomorrow. So long as she keeps out of there, there's nothing to worry about.
Fliss	Sally said she's still in danger.
Grant	This the invisible woman again?
Fliss	Even if she isn't, we should still think about the next lot of kids that come here.

Haley pops out of the room once more.

Haley	How many steps is there again?
Lisa Gary	Hundred and ninety-nine.
Haley	Cheers.

Haley goes back in.

| **Lisa** | Why don't we just meet up tonight, same time and take it from there? |
| **Fliss** | There's no point unless we know what we're supposed to be doing. |

Mo comes out of Room 11.

Fliss	It's like Bradford Central up here.
Mo	Is Ellie-May in her room, Lisa?
Lisa	Give her a knock.
Mo	(*knocking*) Have youse finished your holiday books, then?

Others nod.

Ellie-May	(*opening her door*) Yes?
Mo	Hiya, we was just wondering if you had a bit of perfume?
Ellie-May	Plenty, thanks.
Mo	Would it be all right if we borrer'd some?
Ellie-May	Erm . . . no.

Ellie-May closes the door.

| **Mo** | Worth a try I s'pose. Aren't you lot getting ready? |
| **Lisa** | We're going like this. |

Mo   You can borrow some of me and Joanne's stuff if you want.

Lisa   Thanks, Mo.

Mo returns to Room 11.

Fliss   Just imagine Hepworth's face if we'd all written about this lot.

Gary   'Today, we went to St Mary's Church at the top of the East Cliff, it was great but the best bit of our holiday was when Ellie-May Sunderland became one of the undead . . .'

They laugh.

David   (*off*) Any teachers up there?

Gary   They're all downstairs, mate.

David   (*entering*) What's so funny?

Lisa   They're being stupid.

Gary   We're deciding what to do about tonight.

David   Sounds to me like this old woman of yours wants you to kill him for her.

Gary   Ten out of ten!

Lisa   And how are we supposed to do that?

Haley pops out again.

Haley   Sorry.

Lisa   What is it this time?

Haley   Steak?

Fliss   (*spelling*) 'e.a.k.'

Haley   Is that the meat or the thing you kill vampires with?

Lisa   Meat.

Haley   I was after the other one, I'm doing about the Dracula place.

Lisa   (*spelling*) 'a.k.e.'

Haley   (*going back in*) Ta, kids.

Fliss, Lisa and David all look at each other. Gary holds up his stick of rock.

Scene Six

The Crow's Nest dining room. Thursday evening.
Music blasts out. Lights go up to reveal a disco
in full swing with the landlady as the DJ. Jo and
Mo are dancing with Ellie-May, copying all of
her moves.

Mr Hepworth   (*to Mrs Evans*) Ellie-May is looking better tonight.

Mrs Evans   Spot of homesickness. The landlady says it happens to a lot of them.

Mr Hepworth   I wouldn't want to leave either if I lived in a house like hers.

Grant   (*joining them*) Do you want to dance, Miss Evans?

Mrs Evans   Oh, this wouldn't be for a bet would it, Mr Cooper?

Grant   (*looking over to his mates who encourage him*) No, Miss.

Mrs Evans   Will you excuse me for a moment, Mr Hepworth?

Mr Hepworth   Why certainly, Mrs Evans.

Mrs Evans escorts an uncomfortable-looking
Grant on to the dance floor and struts her
embarrassing stuff.

Waseem   (*laughing*) I don't believe it. She's giving it loads.

Andrew   Glad it's not me up there. He's gone bright red.

Waseem   Hepworth's not pleased.

Andrew   What you on about, he's smiling.

Waseem   No, mate, only looks like he's smiling. He's mad jealous 'cos Grant's dancing with his bird.

Andrew   Mrs Evans? You're joking?

Waseem   She's one of many from what I've heard.

Andrew   Like who?

Waseem   That'd be tellin', wouldn't it.

Jo   (*joining them*) Oh, I'm right dry. Giz a swig of that, Waz.

Waseem   Get your own.

Jo   Charmin'. If you was a gentleman, you'd offer to fetch me one.

Waseem   Pity about me then in't it. (*looking at Grant*) Ahh! She's making him do a waltz.

         While the lads are distracted, Jo signals to Mo who is standing by the door. Mo lets Vicky in. She's plastered in make-up and wearing a fabulous outfit. Mo hurries over to Jo.

Jo   (*acting*) Wow. Get a load of her what's just come in.

         Andrew and Waseem look over. They are impressed.

Waseem   Who is it?

Jo   One of the locals, I think. She must've popped in on her way to a night club or sommats. Sophisticated, in't she?

Andrew   She looks famous.

         Mo joins her.

Jo   Her outfit's fantastic, must have cost a fortune. Look how she's flapping her hair about, Andy. Bet she's got loads of lads after her.

Mo   (*forced whisper*) No need to overdo it!

         Andrew is transfixed. Grant manages to break away from Mrs Evans and comes over.

Grant   Who the 'eck's that?

Jo   (*nudging Mo*) Maybe it's the landlady's daughter.

Mo   (*getting another nudge*) Erm. Yeah. I've heard she's a model in New York.

Waseem   She's coming over.

Andrew   What's my hair like?

Jo	It's great, Andy. You look about eighteen with it like that. Right sexy.
	Mo drags her sister away. Vicky approaches Andrew.
Waseem	(*to Andrew*) She's looking at *you*.
Andrew	I'm sure I've seen her somewhere before.
Waseem	You would have if she's a famous model.
Vicky	(*to Andrew*) Hi.
Andrew	Hi.
Vicky	What are you doing here?
Andrew	I'm er, with my school.
Vicky	(*looking over to the twins who are obviously loving it*) Having me on, aren't you? You look a bit too old for all that.
Andrew	I'm nearly twelve.
Vicky	Hot in here, in't it.
Andrew	Can I get you a drink or something?
Vicky	That'd be great. Thanks. (*to Waseem*) Hi.
	Waseem just grins.
Andrew	What do you want?
Vicky	Tell you what, why don't I decide while we're dancing.
	Vicky takes Andrew by the hand and leads him on to the dance floor.
Waseem	(*jumping up and down*) Ahh! Slaphead!
	Jo and Mo position themselves near Vicky and Andrew on the dance floor, occasionally giving Vicky 'thumbs up' signs. Audience attention is taken by Fliss and the gang.
Gary	Looks like Vicky to me.
David	Yeah, dressed up as a streetwalker?
Lisa	Leave it out, you two. I think she looks great.
Fliss	I think we've got better things to talk about. (*to Gary*) How did you get on with Marriott?

Gary Said she was going to lock it anyway and that I should stop trying to tell her how to look after someone.

Fliss Have you made your minds up yet?

Gary Go in there? Joking, aren't you?

Fliss Have you got a better idea?

Lisa I have. We go to bed tonight like everybody else and forget about it.

Fliss And what about Ellie-May and all the other kids he's got hold of?

Gary We've done our best. Everyone's having a good time except us, it's been the same all week. This lot have all been on holiday while we've been stuck in some sort of nightmare. Why have *we* got to be the ones to do something?

Fliss I just think we've been picked out somehow.

Gary *You* might have been.

Lisa You're the one who spent hours sucking that stick of rock till it got a point on it. You're part of it whether you like it or not.

David We're all scared, mate.

Fliss So, what's it to be then?

Gary I'll do it.

Lisa Right. Let's forget about all this for a couple of hours and at least pretend to be having a good time. Well, come on, it might be the last chance we get.

Lisa drags the others on to the dance floor. Andrew and Vicky are having a rest in another part of the room.

Andrew I knew I'd seen you somewhere before.

Vicky Had you going for a bit, though.

Andrew Yeah.

Clumsy pause. They both try to speak.

Vicky	You first.
Andrew	No, you.
Vicky	I was just going to say, bet you won't want anything to do with me now you know who I am.
Andrew	It is a bit embarrassing.
Vicky	(*suddenly on the verge of tears*) Thanks!
Andrew	No, I mean with me ignoring you and that. I never realized you were erm . . .
Vicky	What?
	Andrew whispers something to Vicky. She pulls back and screams with delight.
Vicky	(*shouting*) Mo! Joanne! He just called me a woman.
	The twins applaud. Vicky runs over to them. Andrew joins Waseem and Grant.
Waseem	I thought you'd've snogged her by now, mate.
Andrew	We're taking it slow.
Grant	So, what part of New York is she from?
Waseem	They were winding him up. It's Vicky Holmes with a wig on.
Grant	Never!
Andrew	It's not a wig, it's backcombed. Anyway, you gonna tell me about Hepworth's other girlfriends or what?
Grant	Hepworth's got a girlfriend?
Andrew	Whole army of 'em according to Waz here.
Waseem	Obvious when you think about it.
	Mrs Marriott loiters behind them.
Waseem	If he doesn't have at least ten on the go at once, he goes off his head. (*to Grant*) You ought to watch it, mate! Mrs Evans is one of 'em!
	Mrs Marriott's attention is grabbed.
Grant	Nah!
Waseem	Been seeing her for years, yeah. Started working his way round rest of staffroom then.

Mrs Marriott's eyes widen.

Andrew   He's making it up.

Waseem   No, it's true! Look at his head if you don't believe me. Not a hair in sight!

Grant   And he's been through every teacher in our school?

Waseem   Every teacher in Bradford.

Grant   He'd be done for if Marriott found out.

Waseem   Already knows, mate. She's one of his favourites.

Mrs Marriott   Waseem Kadeer!

Lights snap to black. Music stops suddenly.

Scene Seven

Top floor landing of The Crow's Nest. Late Thursday night. David, Fliss, Gary and Lisa stand inside the bathroom.

Fliss   Have we got everything?

Others show their various things. Fliss looks at her watch.

Fliss   Not long to go now.

David   Soon be over.

Gary   One way or the other.

Fliss   We're going to win, Gary.

Gary   If you say so. But if someone had told me last week I'd be risking my neck for Ellie-May Sunderland, I'd have told him he was nuts. I don't even like her.

Lisa   Who does?

Fliss   Let's go.

David inches towards Room 13 with the plastic cross from his kite held out in front of him. Lisa walks directly behind him, torch in hand.

David   Remember to shine it in his eyes if he's already awake.

Lisa   I know what I'm doing, Trotter.

Gary and Fliss follow up the rear. The town clock starts to strike twelve as, once more, the number 13 appears on the cupboard door.

Fliss   Is everyone OK?

Lisa   Never felt better.

The organ starts to drift in.

David   Any time now.

There is a hammering noise.

Grant   What the . . .

Mrs Marriott (*off*) Ellie-May Sunderland, get back into bed this instant.

Mrs Marriott lets out a yelp as though Ellie-May had tried to hurt her. The door to Room 13 opens inwards.

David   We'd better get this over with.

Grant   Yeah, before Ellie-May hammers her way out of there.

They advance forward and walk into Room 13. Ellie-May still hammering. Lights begin to fade down.

Mrs Marriott Your parents will be hearing about this, young lady. Let go of me! Ellie-May, for the last time . . . Ouch!

Scene Eight

Inside Room 13. Streaks of coloured light shine in through the window. There is a coffin close by, and what appear to be statues standing in the darkness. The beam of Lisa's torch finds a coffin.

Gary   Is he still in there, do you think?

David   Only one way to find out, mate. Can you see anything, Lisa?

Lisa   Only cobwebs.

Fliss   OK. Let's get it open.

Fliss and David start to pull at the coffin lid. Lisa shines her torch around and catches one of the statues in its beam. It appears to be of a soldier from the First World War. Lisa screams, making the others jump violently.

Gary   What is it?

Lisa   There, in the shadows.

Fliss   It's just a statue, Lise, shine it over here.

Lisa   Its eyes moved, I saw them. I think we should get out . . . now!

David   It'll be a trick of the light. It's starting to move now, Fliss.

The coffin lid comes away a little. Fliss and David have to stand back.

David   It stinks!

Behind them, the figure begins to twitch and then stiffly walk towards them. Others also appear from the darkness. Some are soldiers, others children, wearing tatty clothes from different periods of time.

Fliss   One last shove should do it. Is everyone ready?

Grant   As we'll ever be.

Lisa tries to talk but all that comes out is a squeak. She's seen the figures moving towards them.

Grant (*to Lisa*) We haven't even started yet, Lisa, try to stay calm . . . (*he sees the figures and starts to panic*) I think you should take a look at this!

David We're done for.

Fliss Don't just stand there, the cross!

David holds the cross up to the figures closest to them. The figures cower away from it, hissing and gurgling.

David If you're going to do it, now would be a good time. Please.

Lisa I feel sick.

The coffin lid comes away. The Beast is wearing a dirty shroud. He is thin and grey with his bony hands folded across his chest.

Fliss Put it between his fingers.

Lisa shines the torch on his hands as Grant positions the point of his stick of rock.

Grant OK, Fliss. Now!

Fliss lifts the piece of stone. The Beast's eyes open.

Lisa He's waking up.

The figures are starting to surround them. David is having trouble warding them off. Fliss raises the stone once more.

Beast No!

Lisa⎱ Yes!
Gary⎰

David I can't hold them back any longer.

Lisa Do it, Fliss!

Fliss brings the stone down, ramming the makeshift stake into the heart of the Beast. He bucks, hisses, and cries out. Dust and pieces of masonry start to fall from the ceiling. The figures writhe and wail before falling to the ground.

Grant   The door!

Lisa   It's starting to close.

David   Run for it!

They drop their things and make a dash for the door. There is an almighty rumbling as the light from the window grows brighter, the sound of glass shattering rips across the stage as the window disappears from view. Silence.

Scene Nine

The Crow's Nest car park. Friday morning. The group appear from the main entrance with their bags and are taking them towards the other side of the stage. Andrew and Vicky are standing together in a world of their own. Mrs Marriott gives a blast on her whistle. She has scratches on her face and her arm is in a sling.

Mrs Marriott   The coach driver can only load one item of luggage at a time. Please form an orderly queue and wait your turn. Felicity Morgan!

Fliss   Yes, Mrs Marriott.

Mrs Marriott   I'd like a word, please. Bring your friends with you.
Fliss and the gang go over to her.

Vicky   (*laughing*) You're dead hilarious, Andy.

Andrew   Yeah.

Mrs Evans   Quite the little Romeo.

Mr Hepworth	And ready to 'settle down', according to Vicky.
Mrs Evans	Good advice. Perhaps you should bear it in mind. Might put a stop to the gossip.
Mr Hepworth	Oh.
Mrs Evans	I wonder if Juliet had a whistle?
Mr Hepworth	Yes, very funny.
Mrs Evans	Might as well get used to it, Mr Hepworth, it'll be all round school by Monday.
	Waseem enters from the hotel carrying three large suitcases. He can hardly walk.
Mr Hepworth	Not if he knows what's good for him. I'm glad to see *you're* taking it so well.
Mrs Evans	Me, Mr Hepworth?
Mr Hepworth	Didn't she tell you that part? You were one of my first, apparently.
Mrs Evans	(*suddenly furious and heading for Waseem*) Move it, Kadeer! And once you've taken those to the coach, you can help everyone else with theirs.
Waseem	(*worried*) Yes, Miss.
Mrs Marriott	(*talking to Fliss and the gang*) . . . I don't know what's been happening and I dare say I wouldn't wish to. All I ask is an assurance from each of you that once we've left this place, the whole thing, whatever it is, will be forgotten.
Gang	Yes, Mrs Marriott.
Mrs Marriott	Very well.
	Mrs Marriott leaves them.
Lisa	I don't believe it. The noise we made last night was enough to wake the dead and she's letting us off just like that.
David	By the state of that arm, I'd say Ellie-May tried one of her 'Demon Specials' on her.
Fliss	She knows something's gone on.

David	Yeah, but she's too scared to admit it.
	Ellie-May joins them.
Fliss	Damn! I didn't get a present for my mum.
Ellie-May	I wanted to say thanks. I know something's happened.
Fliss	It's all right Ellie-May, you don't have to explain.
Ellie-May	I feel different, better sort of. I know it must have been something bad and I know you all did something to help me.
Gary	You were just sleepwalking, Ellie-May.
Ellie-May	Thanks, anyway.
	Ellie-May turns to walk away. Then she remembers something and stops. She takes a small box from her coat pocket, walks back and hands it over to Fliss.
Ellie-May	Give this to your mum if you like.
	Ellie-May makes her way over to the coach. Fliss opens the box.
Gary	Wonders never cease.
Lisa	What did she give you?
Fliss	It's one of those little glass ducks.
Mrs Marriott	(*whistle blast*) Into the coach, please, everyone.
Grant	Miss?
Mrs Marriott	What now, Cooper?
Grant	(*pointing up at the hotel*) I think we've left someone behind. Standing up at the window, look.
Haley	She's too young to be with us.
Jo	Look at way she's got her hair, it's like sommat out of olden days.
Grant	There's someone with her an' all.
Mo	I wonder what room they was in. You think we'd have seen 'em before.

Vicky They're waving, look. (*to Andrew*) Shall we wave back, Andy?

Andrew waves, others start to join in.

Lisa Not waving to the old women, Fliss?

Fliss Don't know what you're talking about. (*picking up her bags*) We getting on this coach or what?

The End

Before you Read

On pages viii–ix, there is a list of characters with a brief description of each. You may find this useful until you get to know the characters through the course of the play. The questions that follow this section should also help you to keep track of the story as it progresses.

Helpful Play-reading Tips

- If reading in a group, listen to everyone else. Don't just wait for your character to speak.
- Always read the stage directions. Actions speak louder than words.
- Try to imagine yourself as the audience. This play was designed to be performed.
- If reading on your own, try to create a 'mind cast'. Think of suitable actors for the various parts and imagine them performing the dialogue especially for you.
- Sometimes characters do not say what they are feeling. When in doubt, ask the following questions. What are they saying? What do they mean? What do they want?
- Have faith. To get the best out of a play, you should allow yourself to believe in the story. Try to lose yourself in the world it creates. Once you manage this, your imagination can work miracles.

To Get in the Mood

The Mind Journey

On the next page there is a group exercise to be led by a teacher or director. Choose a piece of haunting music. The group must be relaxed, quiet and prepared to listen. Explain that you will be asking questions that do not require verbal answers. Use the following points as a guide to help create atmosphere.

- You are in a dark, mysterious place. A single streak of light shines down through a small hole in the wall. It creates a tiny oval of brilliant white on the dusty floor beside you.
- Your eyes are getting used to the darkness now. You can make out shapes in the room. They appear to be moving.
- Have you been to this place before?
- What does this room smell like?
- A cold breeze blows across your face and something rustles behind you.
- You stand up and look around.
- There are three doors. Each one is slightly different from the next.
- Go inside one of them. Feel the door as you open it. It feels colder than the rest of the room.
- There is a figure on the other side of the door. Do you know who it is?
- The hair on the back of your neck stands up.
- The figure points in your direction. You feel a hand clamp down on your shoulder.
- You can just make out the tips of the fingers from the corner of your eye. What are they like?
- Your mouth becomes dry.
- You try to move but the hand is pushing your body into the floor.
- Stop the music and create the sound of an alarm clock.

Go around the group inviting each person to talk a little about how he or she felt. Do not encourage comment until everyone who wants to speak has done so. Point out the importance of listening to what people have to say. This exercise is designed to stimulate the senses by using the imagination. Try to steer the discussion in this direction and see if any discoveries have been made. Ask the group to bear in mind these discoveries, thoughts or feelings as they begin to experience *The Play of Room 13*.

Questions and Explorations

Keeping Track

Act One

Scene One
1 What is the audience being told about the mood of the play?
2 Can you predict anything about the play after reading the verse?

Scene Two
1 Which of the three teachers is in charge?
2 What does the comb tell us about Andrew?
3 What does Mrs Evans think of Vicky?
4 Why does Fliss say she feels as if she's already been to Whitby?
5 Where does this scene take place? How is the audience told?

Scene Three
1 What things does the verse make you think about?
2 Why are the little girls there?
3 Who do you think the girls are?

Scene Four
1 What sort of person is Ellie-May? Why do you think this?
2 How many steps lead up to the Abbey on top of the cliff?
3 What does the hotel look like?
4 How many words are used to describe the hotel?
5 How are Fliss and Lisa different from the boys?

Scene Five
1 What does this scene tell you about Jo and Mo?
2 Who has the greater opinion of themselves?
3 Who would you most like to be friends with?
4 Where is the 'punchline' in this scene?
5 When and how was the joke set up?

Scene Six

1 Why do you think the verse from Scene One is repeated while Fliss is asleep?
2 How many different sound effects are heard?
3 What difference do these effects make to the scene?
4 What is the first thing you think of when you read the words, 'Tall, caped figure'?
5 Who do you think the girl is?
6 What word best describes the feeling you get when waiting for the figure to approach Fliss?
7 Why would Mr Hepworth have a towel draped over his head?

Scene Seven

1 What is a drover?
2 How is the audience told about where this scene is set?
3 Why does Vicky say she loves caravan sites?
4 What is the relationship between Ellie-May and Mrs Marriott?
5 Why does Fliss say 'Two on eleven . . .' and where do you think she heard it?
6 Why does Lisa snap at Fliss?
7 What sort of person is Waseem?
8 Why does Fliss grab Waseem by the neck and is this something you would expect from her?
9 David says he went upstairs to use the toilet as someone was having a bath in the one on his floor. Who do you think this was?
10 Before reading this scene, did you know who the girl in Room 13 was?
11 After reading this scene, do you *now* know who the girl in Room 13 was?

Scene Eight

1 Who is the smell of mints coming from and why?
2 Which of the characters do you feel closest to and why?
3 What do you imagine is going on inside Room 13?

Scene Nine

1 Why do you think the old-fashioned girl is sad?
2 What does the verse tell us?

Scene Ten
1 How does the audience know it's the following morning?
2 Why doesn't Mr Hepworth believe Fliss' story?
3 What difference would it make if Mr Hepworth were to believe Fliss' story?
4 What did Lisa see on Ellie-May's neck?
5 How many times does the word 'Dream' appear?
6 Where is everyone planning to go that morning?

Scene Eleven
1 How long ago did the West Wall of the Abbey collapse?
2 Why do you think Mrs Marriott is talking about the surroundings?
3 Who do you think made Mr Hepworth go for the fish and chips?
4 What do you think of Sally immediately after her conversation with Fliss?
5 In Scene Eight, Fliss said she'd heard footsteps outside her bedroom window (see page 19). How does this tie in with this scene?
6 According to Waseem, what happens to boys once they start dating?
7 What is the difference in behaviour between those who know about Room 13 and those who don't?
8 Where is Ellie-May?
9 What is the significance of the line, 'Old stones o'er yonder are not as true as they once were'? (Page 28.)
10 Where is everyone heading after the visit to the Abbey?
11 What does Fliss put into her pocket?
12 What do you think of Sally at the end of the scene?
13 The verse holds a clue about Sally's story. Can you guess what this might be?

Scene Twelve
1 What is the relationship between Lisa and the boys?
2 What is the most exciting moment in this scene?

Act Two

Scene One
1 What does the verse tell us?
2 Are you able to make any predictions about the story after reading the verse?

Scene Two
1 'The Dracula Experience' was mentioned earlier in the play. How was this done?
2 Why were Fliss, Lisa, Gary and David made to sit on the coach all morning?
3 Mo believes the gang were playing rounders the previous night. What are her reasons for believing this?
4 Which of the boys is most eager to believe Waseem's stories?
5 How many days has the school party been in Whitby?
6 Why doesn't Mrs Marriott want the group to cross the bridge into the old town?
7 What do we learn about Fliss?

Scene Three
1 Describe how Fliss might feel when Sally appears to her.
2 What does Sally's line 'what's left of her, anyway' suggest to you? (Page 39.)
3 What was mentioned in the beginning of Act One Scene Seven that has relevance here?
4 How old do you think Sally is?
5 Where in Act One did Margaret first appear?
6 What happens to Sally at the end of this scene?
7 How does Fliss feel at this point?
8 How does this scene bring significance to the verse beginning, 'There stands a tomb . . .'? (Page 42.)
9 Which verse hints at the Sally and Margaret story?

Scene Four
1 What is Jo's and Mo's dad like?
2 What effect would it have on the play if the Jo and Mo characters weren't in it?

3 Jo and Mo didn't talk about getting a present for their mum. What reasons could there be for this?
4 What does Gary say to draw attention to the mystery appearances of the Old Woman?
5 How has Lisa's relationship with Gary and David changed?
6 What reasons can you think of for the absence of Mrs Marriott and Mr Hepworth?
7 When Mrs Evans says, 'you'll be told', how do you think the audience will react?

Scene Five
1 Why does Mo want perfume?
2 How do you think Fliss, Lisa, Gary and David feel as they watch everyone getting ready for the disco?
3 Which piece of verse does the end of this scene bring to mind?

Scene Six
1 Which of the two other teachers does Mr Hepworth get on better with?
2 Why do you think Andrew says, 'She looks famous'? (Page 51.)
3 Who do you think was the master-mind behind the 'Vicky plan'?
4 For the Act One section, you were asked about the difference between those who knew about Room 13 and those who didn't. Has this difference altered?
5 Which of the four (Fliss, Gary, Lisa and David) do you think is the most afraid?
6 What sort of atmosphere is created when Mrs Marriott is listening in on Waseem's story?
7 The Waseem joke was set up in Act One. Can you remember when and how?

Scene Seven
1 Think back through the play. At which points did the gang acquire their various tools?
2 Why doesn't Ellie-May come out of Mrs Marriott's room?

Scene Eight
1 At which two points has the window been mentioned and by whom?
2 What references have there been to soldiers?
3 What aspects bring tension to the scene?

Scene Nine
1 How did Mrs Marriott acquire her injuries?
2 Compare the mood of this scene to Act One Scene One. What are the differences?
3 What thoughts run through Mrs Evan's head between Mr Hepworth saying, 'You were one of my first . . .' and her saying, 'Move it . . .'? (Page 60.)
4 How has Ellie-May changed?
5 What is special about the present Ellie-May gives to Fliss?
6 Who is standing up at the window with Sally?

Overall
1 When did you realize what the various items bought by the gang were going to be used for?
2 At what point did it become obvious that one of the old-fashioned girls was Sally?
3 What was the most frightening part of the play and why?
4 Which part of the play was the funniest?
5 Was there any part of the play that made you feel sad? If so, why?

Explorations

A CHARACTERS

1 Casting Agents
Collect pictures of people from newspapers and magazines and create a cast for *The Play of Room 13*, trying to match the faces to the characters.

2 Questionnaire
The introduction to the characters at the beginning of this play is only intended as a brief guide. The actors portraying these characters must get to know them fully. Choose a character from the play and answer the following questions about him or her. Try to find clues in the text.
- What sort of house does the character live in?
- Describe their home life.
- What is their best subject at school?
- How would they dress for a party?
- Who, on the trip, do they like the best?
- Are they unhappy about anything?
- Who is their favourite pin-up?
- What are they afraid of?
- What is their ambition?
- What do other people think of them?
- What are their hobbies?
- Do they like themselves?
- What is their favourite joke?
- What would it take to embarrass them?

3 Environment
- How someone decorates their house can tell us a lot about their personality. Choose a character from the play, then create a mental picture of that character's bedroom. Try to make this as detailed as possible: imagine the carpet, bed, posters, furniture, books, magazines, toys, games and so on. What sort

of things does this character do when in the room? Where in the house is this room? Does the character live in a house at all?

- Invite a friend into this imaginary room and show him or her around by describing everything there.
- The friend then has to guess the name of the character whose room it is.

4 Hot seat

- Each member of the group selects one of the characters. (If some choose the same one, that's OK.) They take a few moments to think about this character, how they speak, move, laugh and so on.
- They sit in front of everyone, in character, and try to answer any questions the group can think of. If the questions are too difficult, and only then, they can say, 'None of your business' and move on to the next question.
- Discuss what the group have discovered about the characters. Were the answers in keeping with the text?

5 Rules for Improvisation

Below are four situations to explore through improvisation. Before you start, try going through the following rule game.

- Discuss the term 'improvisation', making sure that everyone knows what it means in the context of drama.
- When improvising scenes, the following mistakes often occur.
  a) Backs to the audience.
  b) Actors talking over one another.
  c) Voices too quiet.
  d) Giggling.
  e) Fighting.
  f) Stonewalling.

Stonewalling means that actors are not being co-operative with each other, e.g.

Person 1 Do you like my hat?
Person 2 You're not wearing one!

Encourage members of the group to accept what their fellow actors are giving them and then to build upon it, e.g.

Person 1 Do you like my hat?
Person 2 Yeah, I used to have one like that, where did you get it?

- Divide the group into smaller teams giving two or so of the rules to each one. They then have to improvise a short scene in which these rules are broken.
- The audience can shout 'Stop!' whenever they see a rule being broken and offer a correction.

6 Improvisation Scenarios

Estate Agent

The Crow's Nest Hotel has been put up for sale. The estate agent is showing an interested couple around the old place. One of them has heard rumours of horrible things happening there, but the other doesn't believe in ghosts. The estate agent has to try to sell the hotel to the couple. Make it more difficult by having a ghost (or ghosts) appear.

Sally and Margaret

Re-create a scene (or scenes) from the childhood of Sally and Margaret. Try to capture the feeling of times gone by. Use the things Sally says in Act Two Scene Three as inspiration. Show Margaret going into the domain of the Beast for the first time.

Teachers

At the end of Act Two Scene Two, the teachers go to the pub. Re-create this scene. What do they talk about while they are there? What happens? (Bear in mind that Mr Hepworth and Mrs Marriott don't manage to rejoin the rest of the group that afternoon.)

The Coach

Choose one of the destinations visited in the play. You are returning to The Crow's Nest for tea. Include the following elements: singing, someone being sick, chatting about the trip so far. The coach stops. There is a ghostly figure standing in the middle of the road. The driver becomes possessed and starts to drive towards the edge of a cliff.

7 Screen to Stage
In groups, take turns to talk about your favourite film. Identify the parts of each film that made the greatest impact. Work out how the same impact could be made if you had to present it to a live audience. Bear in mind that expensive sets and special effects are not an option!

8 The Dracula Experience
- Read through Act Two Scene Three up to the point where Fliss is left on her own.
- Rehearse and perform this section.
- Concentrate on creating an atmosphere of fear and tension.

B WRITING

1 What is Drama?
In the context of a play, drama is usually about some sort of conflict. This can be between different characters, a character and their situation, a character and their conscience or even a mixture of all of these. A useful rule is:

Character + Problem × Reaction = Drama

If the characters in this (or indeed any other) play didn't face any problems, there wouldn't be much worth watching. Who wants to see a gang of people being happy and contented all the time?
- This rule can either be used in the play as a whole or with the individual scenes as in the example below.

Act One Scene Six
a) Fliss is the person we identify with.	**Character**
b) She hears noises.	**Problem**
c) She becomes frightened.	**Reaction**
d) The audience is engaged.	**Drama**

- Look at the following scenes and discuss how they fit this rule.
  Act One Scene Ten
  Act One Scene Twelve
  Act Two Scene Five
- See if you can spot this basic idea at work in the play as a
  whole, using Fliss, Lisa, Gary and David as the characters.

2 Sally's Story
Throughout *The Play of Room 13*, many clues or pieces of
information are given about Sally's story. Go through the text
making appropriate notes, then write her life history, filling in any
gaps that occur.

3 Horror Stories
What is it about horror stories that makes them so compelling? Swap
stories in the group and discuss which ones are most frightening
and why. (Look over David's ghost story in Act One Scene Two.)

4 Vampire Stories
Do you remember the following section from Act One Scene
Eleven?

Gary I still say it's Dracula in there.
Lisa Dracula's just a story, Gary.
David Yeah, but it was taken from real life, Mrs Marriott said.
That fella from Transylvania who stuck people on spikes
and caused everyone to have a blood shortage. It could
be him up there.

Mrs Marriott could have been talking about a historical character
called Vlad Dracul, known as 'Vlad the Impaler'. He lived in
Rumania, in eastern Europe, during the fifteenth century and was
called the Impaler because he used to skewer his enemies on
long sharp stakes and leave them to die slowly. According to
legend, shortly after Vlad's death an epidemic of anaemia swept
through the country. This condition, which leaves people pale
and constantly exhausted, is most usually caused by lack of iron
in the diet, but the superstitious peasants believed that Vlad was
sucking their blood to prolong his own existence.

Some people believe this story to be the origin of the vampire legend. Why do you think vampires have captured the imagination of so many generations since those times? Try writing your own vampire story, using the following rules as a guide.

- Introduce the character(s) and show us a little of their everyday life.
- Introduce the idea of the vampire.
- Show your character(s) getting closer to the vampire.
- What happens when they meet up?
- Make the situation more frightening.
- Have a big moment!
- Rescue your character(s).
- End the story by showing how the characters have changed. For example, you might have told us early in the story that the characters like to tell vampire stories to frighten people. After their experience, they might think twice.

Once your story is written, see if it fits the rule given in Section 1 on page 74.

5 Journals
- Discuss as a group the sorts of things that would go into the various characters' holiday journals.
- Select a character who knows about 'Room 13' and another who doesn't. Write contrasting excerpts from their journals.

6 Postcards
- Write a postcard from a character of your choice.
- Think about who it is sent to and allow this to influence your work. Remember that we tend to choose different types of vocabulary for talking or writing to different people.

C PRODUCTION

Although a lot of enjoyment can be found in reading plays, their real purpose is to act as a blueprint for a live performance. In this section, we will be looking at what would be needed in order to put

The Play of Room 13 on stage. It takes a lot of energy and commitment to achieve such a goal, not to mention team work. Below, the workforce has been divided into the following groups.

- **Set Design**
- **Wardrobe**
- **Props**
- **Special Effects**
- **Multi-media**

Before work begins, those involved in the play's production should be divided into five to make the above groups. Each group should work alone at first, following the guidelines below and then share their ideas with the others.

1 Set Design

Imagine you are a professional design team. Your producer has given you a copy of *The Play of Room 13* and asked for sets to be designed for each of the locations. You have a very low budget, so huge West End-style sets are out of the question. When asked for advice, the producer has simply said, 'Less is best!'

Things to consider
When watching a play, there is nothing worse than long, laborious scene changes. You need to come up with ideas for things that are quick to get on and off the stage.

Things to do
- Find out how many different locations are used in the play.
- Find out how much time you will have to make the necessary scene changes. (In many cases, the playwright will have engineered the beginning or end of scenes to make this job easier. Look out for how this has been done in *The Play of Room 13*.)
- Draw sketches of how you would like your sets to look.
- Draw a plan of your stage. (Have one copy for each location.) Now draw your sets on to these plans.
- Ask the Multi-media team if they need sets or backdrops for their video sequences.
- Prepare a presentation of your ideas for the other teams.

Suggestions from the playwright
Here are some of the ideas the playwright had when putting the play together on the page. Of course, you may be able to improve upon these.
- Have several free-standing, vertical panels that can be moved easily around the stage (perhaps on castors).
- Have a door in each panel that is capable of opening both inwards and outwards.
- Once put together, one side of the panels can be used to create the landing of The Crow's Nest.
- The other side of the panels can be used to create other locations.
- Use glue, paper and chicken wire to create the ruins of the Abbey. (Talk to members of the Special Effects team about how to make the chunk of stone fall off, as in Act One Scene Eleven.)

2 Wardrobe
It is your job to decide what each of the characters in *The Play of Room 13* will wear. It is also your responsibility to design make-up.

Things to consider
There are several non-speaking roles in the play. We need some extra members on the school trip and characters from 'The Dracula Experience'. Don't forget the soldiers. You also need to be aware of how much time your actors have between scenes to get in and out of their costumes. Look to see how the playwright has tried to make this easier.

Things to do
- Make a list of all the main characters.
- Make a list of the non-speaking characters.
- Look for clues in the script as to what they may be wearing.
- Sketch your designs, including make-up where necessary.
- Prepare a presentation for the other teams.

3 Props

The term 'props' is short for properties. It refers to all the things, except sets and costumes, that your actors will need to perform the play.

Things to consider
Take note of everything: nothing is insignificant. The comb needed for Act One Scene Two is just as important as the stick of rock appearing in Act One Scene Four. Also, is this the same stick of rock that is used in Act Two Scene Five?

Things to do
• Fill in a chart like the one below:

SCENE	CHARACTER	PROP

• Make a props list for each of the actors.
• Decide where these props can be obtained from.
• Write a list of the props that need to be made.
• Work out how those props are to be made, listing the materials required.
• Prepare a presentation for the other teams.

4 Special Effects

It is your team's job to come up with simple yet effective ways of making the more unusual things in *The Play of Room 13* come to life. Your producer has asked for ideas that won't cost too much money but that will still manage to convince the audience.

Things to consider
Remember, the simpler the better. Make sure your ideas are safe for the actors. Check with your Set Design team, so that you don't end up working on the same things.

Things to do
- Make a list of all the special effects needed.
- Suggest a few ideas to the rest of the team, then try to simplify them.
- Draw diagrams to illustrate how your ideas will work on stage.
- Prepare a presentation for the other teams.

Suggestions from the playwright
Here is one idea for the number 13 appearing on the door.
(Of course, you might be able to come up with a better suggestion.)
- Draw the number 13 on the door, making it big enough to be seen by people at the back of the auditorium.
- Cut the numbers out as though you were making a stencil.
- Make a frame behind the cut-out numbers, so that a piece of card can be slotted in.
- Slot in a piece of card that is the same colour as the front of the door.
- Fix a coloured light to the back of the door.
- When the card is removed, the number 13 will appear.
- Make sure that the door opens inwards with the number still facing the audience. This way, the audience won't see the light or the person operating the device. (A different door may be needed in Act One Scene Ten for Mr Hepworth.)
- Talk to your Set Design team about this.

5 Multi-media
You are responsible for the sound effects, lighting effects and video sequences.

Things to consider
Sound can make a huge difference to a scene, whether it's sinister organ music, seagulls or gently lapping waves. You are the creators of atmosphere! Remember to check things out with the Special Effects team – you may need each other's help. For the video sequences, the Tourism and Leisure Department of Scarborough Borough Council (Tel. 01723 232323) has a video of Whitby available for purchase and a library of 35 mm colour

transparencies of Whitby, which can be borrowed against a modest returnable deposit. The copyright-holders are happy to license the use of both video and transparencies in public performances of *The Play of Room 13* by schools.

Things to do
a) Sound
   • Make a list of the sound effects needed.
   • Work out how to create the sounds. Should they be performed live or pre-recorded?
   • Note how long the various sounds need to run and how many times they are used.
   • Prepare a short presentation.

b) Video
   • Make a list of all the video sections in *The Play of Room 13*.
   • Draw storyboards for each section. (A storyboard is like a comic strip drawing.) Consider how the finished film will look.
   • Do these sections need sound or music?
   • Will you require sets or backdrops?
   • There may be scene changes happening on stage while your video sequences are being shown. Your Set Design team may need to know how long your sections run.
   • Prepare a short presentation describing the ideas.

c) Lights
   • Make a list of all the lighting requirements. Remember, a beach scene will be bright and sunny (yellow perhaps?), and a horror scene may need shadows and a lot of blue and red.
   • Offer help to the Special Effects team.
   • Prepare a short presentation.

6 Presentations
Each team now make their presentation to the group, allowing time at the end of each one for question and answers.

D OTHER ACTIVITIES

1 Postcards
Draw a suitable scene or picture to go with the postcards written earlier (see page 76). Again, bear in mind who the card is intended for. (Granny might not appreciate blood, gore and vampires.)

2 Publicity Leaflet
In Act One Scene Four, David finds a leaflet advertising 'The Dracula Experience'. Recreate this leaflet, adding to the words he reads out. Include pictures.

3 Stained Glass Windows
- Most stained glass windows tell a story. What story do you think the great window in the domain of the Beast would tell? Draw this window. Perhaps your Set Design or Special Effects teams have already given you some ideas? If not, work from the clues in the script and, of course, your imagination.
- Try making a model of your window using black card and coloured film or tissue paper.

4 Timetable
Draw up a timetable for the week, starting on Monday morning at school, when the coach leaves for Whitby. Go through *The Play of Room 13* and look for clues. What did everyone do on each day and when? Bear in mind that Mrs Evans is teasing Vicky in Act One Scene Two when she talks about all the things they'll be doing on their first afternoon.

5 Stage Your Own Production!
If you've done all the preparation, why not put it to use?